DINOSAUR STAMPS

OF

THE WORLD

Dedicated to the memory of L Beverly Halstead, D.Sc. 1933 - 1991

ACKNOWLEDGMENTS
The author would like to thank the following:
The Royal Mail for permission to reproduce the commemorative set of 'Owen's Dinosauria' stamps and the August 20th 1991 first day cover. Professor Bryan Kneale, the stamp designer, for autographing the first day cover.
The Illustrated London News Picture Library for permission to reproduce the illustrations on pages 8 and 10.
For loan or gift of stamps, miniature sheets and/or first day covers - Dr Ron Austin, Dr Peter H.von Bitter, Philatelic Bureau, Falkland Islands, Mr Mike Howgate, Dr Simon Kelly, Mr Stephen King, the Geology Department, National Museum of Wales, Dr Bob Owens, Mr Howard Rosen and Dr Andrew Scott.
For help with data, identifications, greek translations and systematic queries - Mr Mick Bolstridge, Sandra Chapman, Dr Arthur Cruickshank, Mr Mike Howgate, Dr Angela Milner, Professor Dick Moody and Dr David Norman.
A particular thank you goes to Dr Ron Austin who has fed me with data on an almost daily basis and to Dr David Norman for reading through the plates text, putting me right on a few points and for writing the preface.
My secretary Patricia Norgan for data entry, index compilation and proof reading.
I am especially grateful to Dr Helen Haste for allowing me access to the late Bev Halstead's notes and library.
Finally, special thanks to my wife Pam for her support and tolerance over the last four months of frenzied dinosaurian activity.

ISBN 0 9508063 4 X   First edition, first issue, August 1991.

Cover design, artwork and design by Jenny Halstead

Inside front cover cartoon by Richard A Baldwin

Typesetting by T Sue Ryder

Printing and production by Benfoy Press, Witham.

Published by: **Baldwin's Books**
Fossil Hall, Boars Tye Road, Silver End, Witham, Essex, England, CM8 3QA.   Telephone (0376) 83502   Facsimile (0376) 84480

DINOSAUR STAMPS

OF

THE WORLD

With kind regards

Stuart A Baldwin

July 2018

By

Stuart Baldwin and Beverly Halstead

1991

PREFACE

As hobbies go, stamp-collecting must rank near the top of any shortlist. As subjects go, dinosaurs also rank pretty near the top of most people's list of fascinating topics. I do not know quite how book publishers decide what will or will not sell, but it strikes me that putting these two subjects together in a book about dinosaurs which appear on postage stamps is a pretty shrewd move.

As a palaeontologist specialising in research on dinosaurs, and an extremely badly organised but enthusiastic collector of stamps, I could not help but notice the occasional appearance of small poster displays of dinosaur postage stamps at palaeontological meetings around the country in recent years. Nothing large, just a few here and there, and usually the products of rather exotic places around the globe. I knew there were a few dinosaur stamps of course, but was not at all prepared for the number which have been brought together in this wonderful volume by Stuart Baldwin and the late Beverly Halstead.

Palaeontologists like myself will find this subject irresistible for a number of reasons. Yes... dinosaurs are fascinating and many of us collect dinosaur paraphernalia, including dinosaur postage stamps, in the same way that we search out and collect fossil bones; but it is quite staggering, and a tribute to Beverly and Stuart's perseverance, to see how many countries have featured them (and other fossil creatures as well as plants) on their postage stamps. I also have to admit to a rather perverse fascination in searching through the stamp illustrations (in typical academic fashion) for error in anatomy or posture - to test myself as much as anything; to examine the frequency with which some appear; and also to see how gloriously appropriate (or inappropriate!) the choice of the dinosaur may be for a particular country; or just how "artistic" the interpretation of the dinosaur might be. Philatelists will equally find joy in this compilation since it holds a wealth of fascinating information on a poorly covered philatelic area.

The timing of this book is just about as perfect as anyone could have managed. This year is the 150th anniversary of the naming of dinosaurs in Britain, and will see a number of dinosaur celebrations. Not the least amongst these will be the launch of a commemorative series of dinosaur stamps by the Royal Mail in August 1991. Here my tenuous link with stamps is reinforced as I was fortunate to sit with Sir David Attenborough, Dr Robin Cocks (Keeper of Palaeontology at the Natural History Museum) and Dr Beverly Halstead, on a special committee convened by the Royal Mail to consider these stamps.

Tragically Beverly Halstead, who was foremost amongst the committee in pushing for a commemorative series of dinosaur stamps, was killed in a traffic accident earlier this Summer. Stuart Baldwin has ably supervised the completion of this book which he and Beverly started together. And, lest we forget the warmth, humour and indomitable spirit of Beverly, Stuart has very generously offered to donate all author's royalties from this book to the *Beverly Halstead Trust Fund*. I can think of no better or more appropriate tribute to a man who gave so much for his chosen science.

David Norman (Cambridge, 1991)

CONTENTS

5

AUTHOR'S FOREWORD

At a Vertebrate Palaeontology dinner last December I had the good fortune to be seated opposite Bev Halstead. The subject of conversation soon turned to Dinosaurs and in particular how he had been instrumental in persuading the Royal Mail to produce a set of Dinosaur Stamps for this 150th anniversary year. Having a small collection of fossil stamps I suggested to Bev that 1991 might be a good year to produce a book on dinosaur stamps. His agreement was immediate and we decided there and then that he would write most of the text while I would track down all known stamps and publish the book.

We decided that its scope should not be restricted to dinosaurs *sensu stricto*, but that it should include any reptiles or amphibians contemporary with or prior to the age of dinosaurs and *Archaeopteryx*. ie. the time scale would be restricted to the Palaeozoic and Mesozoic with nothing after the mass extinction at the end of the Cretaceous Period.

With help from many friends and stamp dealers sets started pouring in, necessitating a somewhat larger book than was originally thought. A number of first day covers have also been included. More would have been shown, but a rush of new issues in the last few weeks meant that several had to be left out.

Bev's style of working was to write everything in one fell swoop. This was planned to be during the first week of May, and at his untimely death at the end of April he had unfortunately only written the section on Owen's Dinosauria and the text for one set of stamps. The original publication date of June 5th (to coincide with the launch of the new Royal Mail stamp designs at the Natural History Museum in London) had to be abandoned. This left the text to be written by me as well (a person far less well qualified than Bev) and I am particularly grateful to the many friends who have rallied round to help with classification queries, identifications and other data, without whom completion would have been impossible. The text has unashamedly been written from the viewpoint of a palaeontologist who knows little of philately. The author hopes however that it will appeal to both palaeontologists and philatelists alike.

The stamps, miniature sheets and souvenir sheets shown on the 96 plates, represent a complete record of all relevant issues known to the author up until the end of June 1991. If there are any omissions or errors please accept my apologies but do let me have details so that possible future editions can be enhanced. The author would also be pleased to hear from any collector or dealer who has relevant issues, first day covers or dinosaur cancellations for exchange or sale.

Finally, if this small offering gives you as much pleasure as it has me in compiling it, then it will all have been worthwhile.

Stuart Baldwin (Witham, 1991)

RICHARD OWEN'S DINOSAURIA

Dinosaurians entered the English language on Friday 30th July 1841, when Richard Owen delivered the second part of his Report on British Fossil Reptiles to Section C (Geology and Physical Geography) of the British Association for the Advancement of Science meeting in Plymouth. Owen spoke for two and a half hours - the audience gave him a standing ovation. As Owen wrote in a letter to his sister "My report gave such satisfaction that the Association voted me £250 for the expense of engraving the drawings, and £200 more for another report".

Giant fossil reptiles were already well known. The Reverend William Buckland had described in 1824 the remains of a giant flesh-eater *Megalosaurus* from Stonesfield, near Oxford. Gideon Mantell, a Sussex doctor, had described the giant plant-eating *Iguanodon* in 1825 and the spikily armoured *Hylaeosaurus* in 1833 from Cuckfield, Sussex. These were simply seen as gigantic lizards and the very first restoration by Buckland of *Iguanodon* is just that.

The genius of Richard Owen was that he realised they were something entirely new. The limbs "more or less resemble those of the heavy Pachydermal species". After listing other details of the skeletons and their combination of both lizard and crocodilian features and "all manifested by creatures far surpassing in size the largest of existing reptiles, will, it is presumed, be deemed sufficient ground for establishing a distinct tribe or sub-order of Saurian Reptiles, for which I would propose the name **Dinosauria**. (Greek *deinos* fearfully great, *sauros* lizard)". With truly remarkable insight Owen stated that "The Dinosaurs, having the same thoracic structure of the Crocodiles, may be concluded to have possessed a four-chambered heart; and, from their superior adaptation to terrestrial life, to have enjoyed the function of such a highly-organized centre of circulation in a degree more nearly approaching that which now characterizes the warm-blooded Vertebrata".

Owen recognised that here were reptiles that stood and walked like mammals with their straight limbs tucked underneath their bodies. From the meagre evidence he had, he restored them with reptilian heads and heavy tails but short trunks. A kind of reptilian rhinoceros. The fundamental feature that distinguishes the dinosaurs from all other vertebrates, is that they were reptiles with the posture and gait of mammals. On this Owen was completely correct and nothing has come to light in the intervening 150 years to alter this one iota.

The detailed account of Owen's speech was published in The Athenaeum on August 21, 1841. "Prof. Owen next proceeded to notice the more remarkable and gigantic forms of terrestrial Saurians .... the *Megalosaurus*, *Iguanodon* and *Hylaeosaurus* described by their original discoverer, Dr. Mantell, and by Dr. Buckland in his "Bridgewater Treatise", much detail is given to the readers of Owen's new observations on the bones. No hint is given of Owen's reasons for separating these three fossil reptiles into a new grouping, nor is his new name the Dinosauria even mentioned.

THE LATE SIR RICHARD OWEN, K.C.B., F.R.S.

There were so many discoveries of prehistoric animals at this time - the giant mammals, the rhinoceros-like *Toxodon*, the camel-like *Macrauchenia*, the armoured *Glyptodon*, and the giant ground-sloth, all collected by Charles Darwin from South America, the giant flightless bird the Moa from New Zealand, the extinct marine reptiles ichthyosaurs and plesiosaurs from the seas of the Age of Reptiles, and the pterosaurs the flying reptiles, and all described by Richard Owen. Dinosaurs were just another astonishing aspect of ancient life of the Secondary Era.

But this was all to change. After the Great Exhibition of 1851 finally closed, the Crystal Palace - an enormous exhibition hall of glass and cast iron - was dismantled and re-erected in Sydenham. Part of the park was to be devoted to geology - then the Queen of the Sciences and far and away the most glamorous subject in the eyes of the Victorian general public. Richard Owen put forward the idea of exhibiting life-sized restorations of extinct animals, and again at his suggestion Benjamin Waterhouse Hawkins was employed as Director of the Fossil Department of the Crystal Palace "to provide examples of everything that can illustrate the science of palaeontologists" (Gardiner, 1991).

So it was that Waterhouse Hawkins modelled Owen a great reptile under the close supervision of Owen himself. Waterhouse Hawkins's great skills brought to fruitition Owen's vision to communicate the awe of prehistoric life to the man in the street. On New Year's Eve 1853 the Illustrated London News had a full page illustration of Waterhouse Hawkins's "The Extinct Animals" model room with the majestic *Iguanodon* dominating and *Hylaeosaurus* with its row of spikes raised. Small mammals scamper over the floor in the foreground and a bird perches on a wooden support.

That same afternoon witnessed the most famous celebratory dinner in the history of science. Again immortalised in the pages of The Illustrated London News. As one of the newspapers of the time recorded it under the headline "Dinner to Professor Owen in the Iguanodon". Waterhouse Hawkins arranged a dinner for 21, eleven of whom sat inside the body of *Iguanodon*, the others at an adjacent table, all beneath pink and white awning with the names of the giants of palaeontology prominently displayed. Owen seated at the head. At his right Professor Edward Forbes composed a song for the occasion:-

Verses for the Dinner in the *Iguanodon*

A thousand ages underground
His skeleton had lain;
But now his body's big and round,
And he's himself again!
His bones, like Adam's, wrapped in clay,
His ribs of iron stout,
Where is the brute alive today,
That dares with him turn out?

An *Illustrated London News* engraving of the banquet held inside the partly built model of the *Iguanodon* on New Year's Eve 1853 at Crystal Palace.

Beneath his hide he's got inside
The souls of living men;
Who dare our Saurian now deride
With life in him again?

(Chorus)   The jolly old beast
                        Is not deceased
                        There is life in him again. (A roar)

Beginning at 4 o'clock this enormous banquet went on late into the night, with large quantities of Sherry, Madeira, Port, Moselle and Claret flowing freely. Owen in proposing the health of their host congratulated him on the accuracy of his models. A fair point as they had been done to Owen's satisfaction in the first place. A very happy band of inebriated gentlemen staggered off into the night. One famous zoologist sadly caught a chill and died.

On June 10, 1854, Queen Victoria opened the Crystal Palace, an event which attracted 40,000 spectators. Charles Darwin, his wife Emma and their children attended as Owen's guests. In the address of the Chairman of the Crystal Palace Company to the Queen, it was stressed that "Professor Owen lent us his assistance in carrying these scientific triumphs a step further and in bringing them down to popular apprehension. Aided by the indefatigable exertions of the modeller, who with his own hands moulded their forms, the gigantic *Iguanodon*, the *Ichthyosaurus* and other monsters of the antediluvian world, will now present themselves to the eye as they once disported themselves and pursued their prey amid the forests and marshes of the secondary and tertiary periods".

The dinosaur models were sensational - the public flocked to see them in their thousands, the world fell in love with dinosaurs and has remained fiercely faithful ever since.

THE PRODUCTION OF ROYAL MAIL COMMEMORATIVE (SPECIAL) STAMPS

In 1840, just one year before the word 'dinosaur' entered our language, Sir Roland Hill introduced the world's first postage stamp, the Penny Black. At the time it was known as a prepaid adhesive label and only became called a postage stamp later. Since then over 200,000 different postage stamps have been issued worldwide. In the UK the major stamps issued up until 1964 were definitive designs usually based on a portrait of the reigning monarch. Some stamps were issued to commemorate special events such as the 1929 Postal Union Congress in London and the 1951 Festival of Britain, but these were few in number.

In 1964 the Post Office was empowered by the then Postmaster General, Tony Benn, to produce more special or commemorative stamps based on the following criteria:-

They should:

Celebrate events of national and international importance

Commemorate important anniversaries

Reflect the British contribution to world affairs including the arts and sciences

Extend public patronage to the arts by encouraging the development of miniscule art

In addition, no subject should detract from the dignity of the monarch whose head traditionally appears on all British stamps, nor should any topic be likely to cause controversy or offence either nationally or internationally.

These criteria still form the basis of issue policy today.

In general about eight sets of UK special stamps are issued annually.

SUBJECT SELECTION

The lead time in subject selection can be as much as 5 years prior to issue. Anniversaries in five years time are looked at and those with a multiple of 50 years are considered. Many suggestions are also accepted from government departments, various organisations and members of the public. The idea of **Owen's Dinosauria** was originally suggested by the late Dr Beverley Halstead with support from many other leading figures in the world of Geology, Palaeontology and Science such as Sir David Attenborough, CBE FRS.

Many hundreds of ideas are then reduced by researchers to a short list of some ten subjects. Two themes are generally mandatory - Christmas and a Europa subject set by the Conference of European Postal and Telecommunications Administrations such as the 1989 'Games and Toys'.

Guidelines for inclusion on this short list are that a subject must be of national importance and have an aspect that is uniquely British. There must be interesting design possibilities and consistency in the subject and visual balance on a year-to-year basis. The only mandatory guideline, however, is that no living person should be depicted other than members of the British Royal Family. The final short list is usually covered by the following themes - The Arts, History, Science, Industry, Flora & Fauna, Transport, Architecture and Christmas. **Owen's Dinosauria** occupies the Science slot for 1991.

DESIGN RESEARCH AND COMMISSIONING

After the themes have been agreed, detailed design work starts in order to determine different approaches for each issue and the choice of designer.

In choosing a designer the selectors look for proven ability to evaluate the concepts of a subject and to produce ideas that are both visually and intellectually stimulating. As many as four designers may be asked to develop a design from different approaches. With **Owen's Dinosauria**, four designers were selected of whom two were asked to produce two alternative sets of designs. These were Brian Kneale, whose designs were selected, Mrs Jenny Halstead, John Larkin and Christopher Wormall. Both the successful designs and the unadopted designs are illustrated in the following pages.

After the different design approaches have been approved by the Design Department of the Royal Mail, they are submitted to the Stamps Advisory Committee which comprises members from fields such as Art, Design and Philately and includes the General Manager of the Royal Mail Stamps and Philately Department, the Head of the Design Department and a Director of the Stamp Printers, Harrison & Sons (High Wycombe) Limited. One of these designs is normally selected for future development and more detailed artwork.

Two mandatory rules apply to special stamps. The Monarch's head at a certain size must be positioned in a clear space at the top left or right corner and always facing towards the centre of each stamp. There must also be a numerical indication of the stamp value. Since 1987, the year of issue has been positioned in the border. The UK is unique in having a Monarch's head to identify its stamps as other postal administrations throughout the world have a requirement to include the name of the country on their stamps.

ESSAYS AND ROYAL APPROVAL

Proofs or essays of the designs are made on a small printing press to check how the artwork reproduces at stamp size and also the fidelity of colour reproduction. In addition it is essential to ensure that the phosphor coating which activates automatic sorting equipment is not obscured. Changes to detail or artwork may have to be made and the seven or eight inks used may have to be strengthened or altered to produce the correct colour combination. This is a reiterative process and as many as four essays may be needed before all the design and operational specifications are met.

When the final essay has been approved by The Post Office and the Stamps Advisory Committee it is submitted to HM The Queen for approval.

PRINTING

The process most used by the Royal Mail for Special Stamps is photogravure though photolithography is used for at least one issue per year. With photogravure the first stage is producing colour separations - a master negative for each of the colours used in the final printing is made up using a series of filters on a camera. These negatives are then used to make multiple exposures on large photographic plates.

The plates are then exposed to intense light in front of sheet film containing many very small gelatine cells. This hardens differentially depending on the amount of light received. The gelatine on the film is then transferred to steel cylinders coated with copper. These are immersed in acid to etch the copper, the less hard gelatine there is the deeper the etching - the cells corresponding to these areas will ultimately hold more ink than others and produce stronger areas of colour on the stamp. Finally the copper is chromium plated and the rolls positioned on a giant press called the 'Jumele'.

Continuous rolls of paper with gum on one side and a coating base on the other incorporating phosphors pass through the cylinders and the ink in the recessed cells is transferred to the paper by electrostatic charges. The paper then passes to a hot-air chamber to dry the ink, followed by a perforator and finally cutters to reduce the paper to sheet size. The press prints over two million special stamps per hour.

THE FIRST DAY OF ISSUE AND MARKETING

Commemorative covers, presentation packs and special events are all part of the marketing leading to the great event - the first day of issue. With **Owen's Dinosauria** a special exhibition was launched at the Natural History Museum in London on June 5th and in August a large model of *Triceratops* featured in various promotional activities.

Outside organisations co-operate with the Royal Mail in these events. e.g. The Geology Section of the British Association meeting at Plymouth and the British National Stamp Exhibitions Autumn 'Stampex' both have dinosaurs as the 1991 theme. A touring exhibition featuring the stamps in this book has also been prepared and will appear at these events and many others.

REFERENCE
Barden, M. 1989. *How Royal Mail Stamps are Produced.* Royal Mail, London.

PALAEONTOLOGICAL PHILATELY An introduction

The zeal of stamp collectors is perhaps only matched by the enthusiasm of those interested in all things dinosaurian. Where these two pursuits can be combined the result is indeed bliss. It was felt that a short account of the history of 'fossil' stamps in general and of dinosaur stamps in particular could be of interest.

It is now exactly forty years ago that the first stamp of a palaeontological nature appeared. A red two anna stamp celebrating the Centenary of its Geological Survey was issued by India in 1951. It shows the fossil 'elephant' *Stegodon ganesa* a probable direct ancestor of our modern elephants.

Since then some 100 different sets containing fossils have been issued including vertebrates, invertebrates, plants, trace fossils, microfossils and Precambrian fossils. Seventy of these sets are represented in this book. As Peter H.von Bitter (1977-78) has shown it is possible to demonstrate various evolutionary sequences. The elephant theme can be followed from *Stegodon* to the mammoths (Romania, 1966, Poland, 1966, Mongolia, 1967) or to the mastodon (Bulgaria, 1971 and Mongolia, 1967). From a common ancestor the line leads to *Dinotherium*, (Romania, 1966, Bulgaria, 1971, People's Republic of the Congo, 1970). Similar themes can be followed for fossil 'man', ammonites - a group of marine cephalopod molluscs that were contemporary with the dinosaurs, trilobites - a group of Palaeozoic marine arthropods, and plants.

Algeria marked the Nineteenth International Geological Congress in 1952 with two stamps, one of which was the second fossil stamp and which featured the ammonite *Berbericeras sikikensis*. Another six years elapsed before the third fossil set appeared from China in 1958 with the world's first dinosaur stamp, (plates 23 and 24) showing *Lufengosaurus* which had been discovered in China in 1930, and at the same time the first trilobite stamp and the first fossil mammal stamp, (plate 24).

For seven years China led the world in dinosaur stamps until in 1965 Poland issued a set of ten Prehistoric Animals containing six dinosaurs, followed closely the same year by San Marino (neither country renowned for their dinosaur discoveries) with a set of nine including six dinosaurs.

Since then sets containing dinosaurs have been issued at an ever increasing rate. For this book anything philatelic showing a dinosaur has been considered appropriate though it is appreciated that a number of issues have not been in postal service, may have been "cancelled to order" and are not considered valid by some. The Tanzania 1991 'Prehistoric Animals' (plates 81-83) is a good example of such a cancellation.

On page 115 a checklist is given, in date order, of all known issues up until the end of June 1991 containing dinosaurs *sensu stricto* on stamps, miniature sheets or souvenir sheets. Of those discovered so far there are 176 dinosaur items out of a total of 288 illustrated, representing 54 issues by 44 different countries or states. On page 116 a graph has been plotted showing the cumulative number of such sets issued against time. From the exponential nature of this curve it can be seen that half of all dinosaur sets issued have been in the last ten years, and that a third were issued in the last five years. From the statistical point of view the result would have been the same had the number of dinosaur stamps rather than sets been plotted. If issues continue at this growth rate then dinosaur stamp collecting is in for a boom period.

ERRORS
These have a particular fascination for the philatelist; a well known one is the missing value from two of the stamps in the Polish 1965 issue. The palaeontologist however can have a field day in this area as mentioned by David Norman in the preface. The most common error is an incorrect spelling or identification. *Edaphosaurus* and *Dimetrodon* are frequently confused. Where these have been detected the correct name is given with underlining of part or all of the word to emphasise the correct version. Errors of posture, position or anatomy are not uncommon - *Brachiosaurus* is shown with its front legs too short in some cases and in deep water in others. Niger have a classic error in that they include dinosaurs under 'Archaeology' and there is a fertile field of investigation for the palaeobotanist as many plants shown are not contemporary with the animal depicted. e.g. The *Stegosaurus* on the 1972 Maldives 2L stamp is from a different time period from the three plants shown.

NOTES ON THE PLATES
As far as can be determined 'Owen's Dinosauria' is possibly unique in that the artwork for the stamps was specially commissioned. Other issues appear to be based on pre-existing artwork by painters such as Z. Burian, J. Gurche, C. Knight, M. Hallett and R. Zallinger. Many sets include other non-reptilian stamps which have not been mentioned. Details of most of these may be found in standard stamp catalogues such as those issued by Stanley Gibbons. All stamps, miniature sheets, souvenir sheets and first day covers are from the author's collection with the exception of those mentioned in the text.

The top ten in terms of frequency of appearance are as follows with the number of appearances given in brackets: *Stegosaurus* (28), *Tyrannosaurus* (18), *Triceratops* (17), *Apatosaurus* (15), *Pteranodon* (14), *Iguanodon* (12), *Dimetrodon* (10), *Brachiosaurus* (9), *Edaphosaurus* (9) and *Rhamphorhynchus* (9).

GREAT BRITAIN
OWEN'S DINOSAURIA 1841. 1991.

Designed by:	Bryan Kneale
Issue Date:	20 August 1991
Price:	5 stamps at 22p, 26p, 31p, 33p, 37p
Format:	35mm x 37mm off-square
Perforations:	14 x 14.5
Paper:	Unwatermarked, phosphor coated with gum PVA Dextrin
Print Process:	Photogravure
Products:	First Day Cover, Postcards (5), Presentation Pack

Iguanodon - the name means 'iguana tooth', was the second dinosaur to be discovered and was one of the three on which Richard Owen based his Dinosauria concept. Some teeth were found by a Mrs Mantell in Sussex, southern England in 1822 and with other remains were described by her husband Dr Gideon Mantell in 1825. Since then many remains and footprints have been found in England, Belgium, North Africa, North America, South America, Spitzbergen and Asia, making it one of the best-known dinosaurs. It was a large ornithopod (bird-footed), plant-eating dinosaur about 33ft/10m long and weighing about 4.5 tonnes, from the early Cretaceous of about 120 mya*. It had large hind legs and shorter forelimbs, both sets of legs having small 'hooves', indicating that it could walk either on all fours, or on its hind legs only with the tail counterbalancing the body. It had a large thumb spike which could have been used to collect vegetation or to defend itself. Mantell only had one thumb spike when he described it and placed it on the snout as a horn - a feature still seen in the Waterhouse Hawkins reconstruction at Crystal Palace Park in south-east London.

*The abbreviation 'mya' is used for: million years ago.

     Pl.1

GREAT BRITAIN
OWEN'S DINOSAURIA 1841. 1991.

Stegosaurus, **Owen's Dinosauria 1841**

Tyrannosaurus, **Owen's Dinosauria 1841**

Stegosaurus - 'roofed lizard', is a well known four-footed ornithischian or 'bird-hipped' dinosaur with a double row of large bony plates embedded in the skin along its back and to half way down its tail. Some of these plates are over 2ft/60cm high. It belongs to a group of armoured dinosaurs called stegosaurs that evolved in the middle Jurassic around 170 mya. They have been found in England, North America, Africa, China, Europe and India. The group had declined by the early Cretaceous but at least one species survived into the late Cretaceous. The stegosaurs were plant-eaters and may have lived in herds. For protection against meat-eating dinosaurs they probably relied on their plates and the long sharp spikes on their tails. *Stegosaurus* was up to 30ft/9m long, typically weighed about 2 tonnes and comes from western North America of about 150-140 mya. Different species have between two and four pairs of tail spikes, some of which were up to 3ft 3in/1m long. The first stegosaurid was found in England and was described by Richard Owen in 1875, while the latest is currently being excavated in the English Southern Midlands.

Tyrannosaurus - 'tyrant lizard', is without doubt the most familiar of all dinosaurs and is the largest flesh-eating land animal known to have existed so far. The saurischia or lizard-hipped dinosaurs are divided into two main groups - the mainly carnivorous two-legged theropods (beast-feet) and the mainly plant-eating four-legged sauropodomorphs (reptile-feet). Of the many groups of theropods, the Tyrannosaurids to which *Tyrannosaurus* belongs, are the most striking. They appeared in the late Cretaceous about 80 mya and died out when the last of the dinosaurs became extinct. As a group they existed for less than 15 million years. Their remains have been found in western North America and Mongolia. *Tyrannosaurus* was about 46ft/14m long and could have weighed up to 7 tonnes. Its skull alone was over 4ft/1.25m long and it had many dagger-like teeth with crowns up to 6in/15cm high, each with serrated edges (as in a steak knife), adapted for cutting flesh. Recent views on its lifestyle suggest that it could have been an active predator capable of short bursts of speed and may also have scavenged. Known only from fragmentary remains for most of this ·century, an almost complete skeleton has just been excavated from the Badlands of Montanna, U.S.A.

Pl.2   18

GREAT BRITAIN
OWEN'S DINOSAURIA 1841. 1991.

Protoceratops - 'first horned face', was one of the earliest of the ceratopians (horned dinosaurs) which evolved in the late Cretaceous. It was a quadrupedal (four-footed) bird-hipped dinosaur about 6ft 6in/2m long with an estimated weight of some 400lbs/180kg. All growth stages from new hatchlings to adults have been found in the Gobi Desert of Mongolia of about 80 mya. Its fame rests on the discovery in the 1920s of nests of *Protoceratops* eggs, the first dinosaur eggs ever found. These eggs were up to 8in/20cm long, were tapered and were laid in clutches of up to 18 in a spiral of 3 tiers. Some eggs had the fossilized bones of baby *Protoceratops* inside them. It had a relatively large heavy skull with a bony neck shield which would have given protection to the neck and served as anchoring points for the jaw muscles. Despite its name it had no horns, though above its eye sockets and on its snout there were thickened bony areas in the positions in which horns developed in later ceratopians. Its hind legs were longer than its fore-limbs and it had a parrot-like beak indicating a possible parrot-dinosaur ancestry.

Triceratops - 'three horned face', is the best-known and also one of the largest and most abundant of the horned dinosaurs. It was up to 30ft/9m long with an estimated weight of between 5 and 10 tonnes - more bulky than a large modern elephant. It had a massive skull up to 6ft 6in/2m long with a short solid bony neck frill. Its nose horn was short and stout but the two brow horns had cores measuring up to 3ft/90cm indicating that the horns themselves must have been somewhat longer. These would have been useful defensive weapons against the contemporary carnivores *Tyrannosaurus* and *Albertosaurus*. From the number of remains found it has been estimated that these plant-eating dinosaurs lived in large herds in western North America from about 70 to 64 mya. The teeth of *Triceratops* and other horned dinosaurs are of particular interest as they are adapted for cutting through very tough plant material. They are arranged in the jaw to give a shear or scissor-like action and are not able to slice or grind. The teeth have wedge-shaped leaf-like crowns and are constantly replaced as they wear out by new teeth pushing up directly underneath the old teeth.

Pl.3

GREAT BRITAIN
OWEN'S DINOSAURIA 1841. 1991.

UNADOPTED AND EARLY BRYAN KNEALE DESIGNS

Tyrannosaurus (unadopted)

Stegoceras (unadopted)

Triceratops (unadopted)

An early *Triceratops* version

Torosaurus (unadopted)

Centrosaurus (unadopted)

Pl.4   20

UNADOPTED JENNY HALSTEAD DESIGNS

Three of the four British dinosaurs shown here are ones that Richard Owen based the term Dinosauria on in 1841. These three each have small illustrations of the models made by Waterhouse Hawkins and which may still be seen today in Crystal Palace Park in south east London. From the scientific point of view, these reptiles on which Owen based his new name, would have been the ideal choice as subjects for the stamps. There are however many considerations other than scientific ones to be taken into account in subject selection and in this case these others have prevailed. *Iguanodon* has been described earlier.

Megalosaurus - 'big lizard', was the first dinosaur to be named and scientifically described - in 1824. It was a large (30ft/9m long) bipedal flesh-eating lizard-hipped dinosaur that lived in the late Jurassic about 140 mya. Its remains and footprints have been found in England and many other countries.

Cetiosaurus - 'whale-lizard', is so called because bones found in Oxfordshire in 1809 were so large they were thought to come from a marine animal. It is a late Jurassic sauropod from about 145 mya - a giant long-necked four-footed plant-eating dinosaur up to 60ft/18.3m long and weighing some 9 tonnes. In the 1980s, a considerable part of a *Cetiosaurus* skeleton was found in Leicestershire and is now on display in Leicester City Museum. It is the most complete British sauropod found so far.

Hylaeosaurus - 'woodland reptile' was found in Tilgate Forest, in southern England in 1833 and was first described by Gideon Mantell. It belongs to a herbivorous group called ankylosaurs - 'fused reptiles', where bones in the skin are fused into sheets of armour plating. Though incomplete it is estimated to be about 13ft/4m long and comes from the early Cretaceous of about 125 mya.

GREAT BRITAIN   OWEN'S DINOSAURIA 1841. 1991.

UNADOPTED JOHN LARKIN DESIGNS

Pl.6   22

GREAT BRITAIN   OWEN'S DINOSAURIA 1841. 1991.
UNADOPTED CHRISTOPHER WORMALL DESIGNS

Iguanodon

Megalosaurus

Cetiosaurus

Hylaeosaurus

Megalosaurus

Iguanodon

Hylaeosaurus

Cetiosaurus

GREAT BRITAIN
OWEN'S DINOSAURIA 1841. 1991.

An official Royal Mail first day cover signed by the artist Professor Bryan Kneale.
The cancellations show a dinosaur skeleton in the rocks.

Pl.8   24

ADEN PROTECTORATE STATES QUATI STATE IN HADHRAMAUT

FOSSIL AND MODERN ANIMALS. 1968.

The green triangular 10 fils stamp shows two dinosaurs in what is now accepted as the classic dinosaur posture with the neck, back and tail sloped to the ground at an angle of 45 degrees. To date no dinosaur has been given the name *Dinosaurus* and these are in fact a large *Tyrannosaurus* in the foreground and the herbivorous duckbilled *Anatosaurus* in the background. These particular restorations are direct copies (but reversed) from a 1938 full colour painting by the Czechoslovak artist Zdenek Burian. The duckbilled dinosaur was identified as *Trachodon*, but this name was based on a single tooth that has never been matched to any skeleton - the restoration is in fact based on a mounted skeleton of *Anatosaurus*.

The other 10 fils stamp is a late Cretaceous scene from North America of about 75 mya, showing the tailless and crested *Pteranodon* in the sky and two giant marine lizards, the mosasaur *Tylosaurus*. This is from a 1941 Burian painting.

Apatosaurus - 'deceipt lizard', a giant quadrupedal plant-eating Jurassic sauropod of about 145 mya, was named by the famous American palaeontologist O.C. Marsh who later invented the name *Brontosaurus* for the same dinosaur. As there cannot be two names for the same animal, the first is the correct scientific name. However brontosaur is used as the common name for the giant sauropods. This again is a copy of a Burian painting, this time from 1950.

Rhamphorhynchus - 'narrow beak', is a flying reptile from upper Jurassic rocks of southern Germany of about 150 mya. It had fish-trap teeth, a 3ft 3in/1m wingspan and a long stabilising tail. It is from a 1941 Burian painting and is based on a specimen which has fine details of the wing membrane preserved.

AFGHANISTAN
PREHISTORIC ANIMALS. 1988.

Mesosaurus

Ceratosaurus

Mesosaurus - 'middle lizard', was a small reptile about 3ft 3in/1m long that had reverted to an aquatic environment. It comes from lower Permian rocks in southern Africa and South America of about 270 mya. Its long flattened tail and strong hindlimbs were adapted for propulsion and it had long jaws with many fine pointed teeth. The illustration is reversed from a 1955 Burian painting.

Ceratosaurus - 'horned reptile' was a large bipedal flesh-eating dinosaur from the late Jurassic of western North America of about 145 mya. Its name is derived from an unusual bony horn on its snout. It also had small bony plates along the centre of its back and tail giving it a serrated appearance. At 20ft/6m long it was much smaller than its contemporary carnivore *Allosaurus*.

Styracosaurus

Styracosaurus - 'spiked reptile' was a large, quadrupedal late Cretaceous north American plant-eating dinosaur of about 80 mya. It measured about 18ft/5.5m, and had a spectacular array of head-horns and spikes - a long snout-horn, a neck frill with strong bony nodules at the sides and six long, sharp spikes projecting out from the rear, providing formidable defensive weapons.

Protoceratops

Stegosaurus

This set from the Robert M. Owens collection.

Pl.10   26

ANGOLA
FOSSILS AND MINERALS. 1970.

Angolosaurus - 'Angola reptile' was a marine
lizard from the late Cretaceous of West Africa of
about 70 mya. It belongs to a group called
Mosasaurs and is related to today's huge land-
lizards, the monitors.

ANTIGUA AND BARBUDA
DISNEY EPCOT CENTER, ORLANDO, FLORIDA. 1988.

Edaphosaurus - 'earth reptile' was a pelycosaur ('sail reptile'), a member of the
Synapsids or mammal-like reptiles from the late Carboniferous and early Permian of
Czechoslovakia and Texas of about 280 mya. It was a herbivore about 10ft/3m long
with a large sail on its back which may have been used for temperature regulation.
The spines supporting the sail had bony cross-pieces.

AUSTRALIA
LIVING TOGETHER. 1988.

The 95c **Law** stamp is one of a set of 27 and
shows a possible evolutionary sequence
including a dinosaur (a cross between a
Stegosaurus and a sauropod?) two mammals, a
lawyer and an unknown futuristic symbol.

27   Pl.11

BELGIUM
NATIONAL SCIENTIFIC INSTITUTIONS. 1966.

Iguanodon - 'Iguana tooth'. Though Mantell first described *Iguanodon* in 1825 is was not until 1877 that its anatomy was properly understood. In the small Belgian town of Bernissart, some coalminers tunnelling underground came across the skeletons of 31 *Iguanodon* in what appeared to be the bottom of an early Cretaceous ravine. It has been suggested that a herd of these could have taken panic stricken flight to escape from a predator and fell into the ravine to their death. These skeletons of *Iguanodon bernissartensis* have now been prepared and are mounted in the Belgian Royal Institute of Natural Sciences in Brussels. Copies of one of the best skeletons are in many museums around the world; in England for example in the Sedgwick Museum, Cambridge and the University Museum, Oxford.

BENIN
PREHISTORIC ANIMALS. 1984.

Anatosaurus

Apatosaurus

Anatosaurus - 'duck reptile', was a plant-eating duckbilled dinosaur belonging to a group called hadrosaurids ('big reptiles'), which evolved in the middle of the Cretaceous Period, probably in central Asia. They subsequently became widespread and diverse. *Anatosaurus* had a toothless horny beak, was about 33ft/10m long and comes from the late Cretaceous of Alberta of about 68 mya.

Pl.12   28

First day cover from the Peter H. von Bitter collection.

BRITISH ANTARCTIC TERRITORY

GONDWANA - CONTINENTAL DRIFT AND CLIMATIC CHANGE.

The study of the relative positions of the continents in past geological periods provides an important contribution to our understanding of the evolution and distribution of prehistoric floras and faunas and hence of dinosaurs. This set shows how the Southern Hemisphere continents were formerly joined in a super-continent called Gondwana and its subsequent division and redistribution over the earth. Three themes are present in the stamps: a palaeogeographic representation of the continents, a colour indicating the prevailing climate, e.g. blue for glaciation, green for cool-temperate, light brown for deserts and orange-red for volcanic conditions, and a feature or fossil typical of the time. Of the latter *Lystrosaurus* is relevant here.

280 million years ago

260 million years ago

230 million years ago *Lystrosaurus*

175 million years ago

Lystrosaurus - 'shovel reptile', shown on the 10p stamp, illustrating 230 mya, was an early Triassic plant-eating mammal-like reptile belonging to a group called dicynodonts ('two dog teeth'). It was about the size of a sheep, had a short tail and legs and a stout barrel-like body and has been called a kind of reptilian hippopotamus. It has been found in Africa, Antarctica, Asia and Europe.

50 million years ago

Present day

BRITISH ANTARCTIC TERRITORY
AGE OF DINOSAURS. 1991.

The issue of this set is an excellent piece of timing by the British Antarctic authorities. From their first appearance on the Earth around 240 mya until their extinction at the end of the Cretaceous Period about 64 mya, dinosaurs were the dominant land animals. This time period is known as **The Age of Dinosaurs**. From the existence of Gondwana as shown in the previous set it had been predicted that dinosaurs should be found in Antarctica. This prediction has been vindicated by recent discoveries of dinosaur remains in the James Ross area of north-eastern Antarctic peninsula in upper Cretaceous rocks of about 70 mya. At that time the climate was considerably warmer there than today.

Late Cretaceous Forest

Hypsilophodont Dinosaur

The 12p stamp shows a **Late Cretaceous Forest**. Though the sediments of James Ross Island are marine in character they do contain remains of fossil leaves (possible dinosaur food) and petrified logs - the remains of plants that grew on a nearby volcanic arc. These were part of cool-temperate Cretaceous forests covering the high latitudes of Gondwana. Southern conifers and the southern beech (*Nothofagus*) were dominant components of the flora. The stamp shows a cross section of a fossil *Nothofagus* tree trunk and a reconstruction of a southern beech forest. Similar forests are found in Tasmania today.

Hypsilophodont 'high ridged teeth' **dinosaur**. The hypsilophodontids are a group of small-to-medium sized fast-running plant-eating ornithopod dinosaurs. As a group they were very successful, evolving in the Middle Jurassic and spreading to all continents except Asia, until their extinction some 100 million years later at the end of the Cretaceous. Typically they were about 5-10ft/1.5-3m long and were probably social animals living in herds. The Antarctic specimen was large - about 16ft 3in/5m long and the remains includes parts of the skull, most of the upper body, neck and part of the hips.

BRITISH ANTARCTIC TERRITORY
AGE OF DINOSAURS. 1991.

An enlargement of the 26p stamp with a 1991 calendar on the reverse, produced for use as a plastic promotional item.

Chlamydoselachus

Mosasaur & Plesiosaur

Frilled Shark *Chlamydoselachus*. Whilst the dinosaurs were exclusively land animals, the sea was the home of many other reptiles and fish including sharks. This one is only included here as it is part of the Age of Dinosaurs Set. As sharks have a skeleton of cartilage rather than bone it is normally only their teeth which become preserved as fossils. As these are constantly replaced throughout life, one shark can leave many hundreds of teeth as fossils. Only one tri-cuspate *Chlamydoselachus* tooth has been found in Antarctica (shown on the stamp) but it is important as it is the earliest record of the genus.

Mosasaur and Plesiosaur. Though no complete skeletons of large marine reptiles have been discovered in Antarctica, their vertebrae and pieces of paddle-like limbs have been found over the last forty years. The Mosasaurs were carnivorous marine lizards related to monitor lizards and the Plesiosaurs, also carnivorous, formed two groups, one with long necks and short heads, the other with short necks and large heads. A long-necked form is shown here. The affinities of the plesiosaurs is uncertain. Both mosasaurs and plesiosaurs lived in coastal waters and probably fed on fish, ammonites or belemnites.

Pl.16   32

BRITISH ANTARCTIC TERRITORY
AGE OF DINOSAURS. 1991.

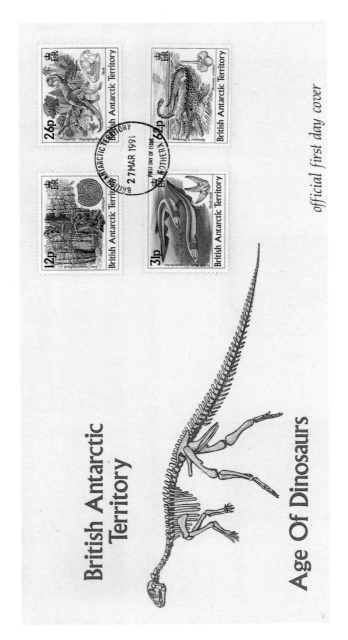

Pl.17

BULGARIA
PREHISTORIC ANIMALS. 1990.

Apatosaurus

Stegosaurus

Edaphosaurus

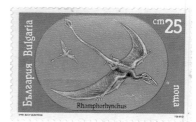

Rhamphorhynchus

Protoceratops

Triceratops

Pl.18   34

CANADA

PREHISTORIC LIFE IN CANADA - 2.

THE AGE OF PRIMITIVE VERTEBRATES. 1991.

This is the second in the series of superb sets from Canada looking at life in Canada from 1,900 mya to about 10,000 years ago. This set looks at two marine life forms and at two of the first land-living organisms. The next set to be issued will be in 1992 and will cover the age of dinosaurs - a set eagerly waited for by collectors. The fourth set will cover the Tertiary/Quaternary.

Archaeopteris

Conodonts

Eusthenopteron

Hylonomus

Conodonts - 'cone shaped teeth', are toothlike microfossils composed of calcium phosphate and are the mouth parts of small primitive eel-like animals. They range from the late Cambrian to the end of the Triassic (about 510-208 mya), and because of their rapid evolution and wide distribution are excellent for dating rocks.

Archaeopteris - 'ancient leaf', is an early giant tree from the Devonian of Quebec and Ellesmere Island of about 360mya. It resembles the conifers of today, had a trunk over 3ft 3in/1m in diameter at the base and reached a height of over 82ft/25m. It formed the first high-crowned forests.

Eusthenopteron - 'strong fin', is a fresh-water carnivorous lobe-finned fish from the Devonian of about 370 mya. It has been found in Quebec and Europe. Its powerful fins may have enabled it to crawl on land and it comes from a group thought to be ancestral to the first land animals, the amphibians.

Hylonomus - 'wood dweller', is one of the earliest-known reptiles fully adapted to life on land. It resembles a modern lizard in both appearance and lifestyle and was about 8in/20cm long. Its remains have been found in late Carboniferous fossil tree stumps in Nova Scotia of about 300 mya, and it probably fed on insects and other invertebrates. It is thought to be ancestral to many groups including the dinosaurs.

CANADA

PREHISTORIC LIFE IN CANADA - 2.
THE AGE OF PRIMITIVE VERTEBRATES. 1991.

A first day cover featuring *Hylonomus* and a *Hylonomus* cancellation.

Pl.20   36

CENTRAL AFRICAN REPUBLIC

PREHISTORIC ANIMALS. 1988.

Apatosaurus

Triceratops

The 50F stamp showing *Apatosaurus* illustrates the point that from the evidence of footprints these large sauropods may have lived in family or group herds. In times of danger the young would probably move to the centre of the group.

Ankylosaurus

Stegosaurus

Ankylosaurus - 'fused reptile', was a large armoured dinosaur with the bones in the skin fused to form protective plates. It was about 33ft/10m long, weighed an estimated 3.6 tonnes and had a heavy bony club at the end of its tail, though this is not apparent in the 100F stamp. It lived in the late Cretaceous of North America about 68 mya.

Pl.21

CENTRAL AFRICAN REPUBLIC
PREHISTORIC ANIMALS. 1988.

Tryannosaurus

Corythosaurus

The *Tyrannosaurus* shows several inaccuracies - e.g. the forelimbs are far too large and the number of digits should be two only. As no forelimbs of *Tyrannosaurus* had been found until recently, it is usually portrayed with very small arms and two digits based on those found in its close relative *Albertosaurus*.

Corythosaurus 'Corinthian helmet reptile' was a very characteristic hadrosaurian dinosaur up to 33ft/10m long with a large rounded crest on the top of its skull. Inside the crest was a network of complex breathing tubes. It comes from the late Cretaceous of North America of about 80 mya.

Allosaurus

Brachiosaurus

Allosaurus - 'strange reptile', was a bipedal carnosaur ('flesh reptile') up to 39ft/12m long. Its skull measured 3ft/90cm and was armed with many serrated edged dagger-like teeth. It was the largest late Jurassic carnivore, weighing an estimated 1-2 tonnes, and lived in western North America about 145 mya.

Brachiosaurus - 'arm reptile' - a very large quadrupedal sauropod dinosaur from the Upper Jurassic of western North America and Tanzania of about 140 mya. It was about 7ft/22.5m long, 39ft/12m high and weighed in at an estimated 80 tonnes, equivalent to some 12 large modern elephants. The front legs are shown far too short here.

Pl.22

CHINA (People's Republic)

CHINESE FOSSILS. 1958.

Lufengosaurus

The Chinese word for dinosaur - 'Konglong', translates as 'terrible dragon' and China today is one of the most prolific areas in the world for new dinosaur discoveries. Well over a hundred species have been described since 1925 and many eggs and trackways have also been uncovered. Large bones have been found in China for many centuries and many early manuscripts refer to 'dragon' bones that we would now call dinosaurs. Bone carvings from the Shang Dynasty (sixteenth to eleventh centuries BC), mention the existence of 'dragons'. The dragon symbolizes both power and justice to the Chinese and a book titled "*Hua Yang Guo Zhi*" by Chang Qu, written in the Western Jin Dynasty (AD 265-317), refers to the discovery of dragon bones at Wucheng in Sichuan province. This could well be the earliest written record of dinosaur bones!

Lufengosaurus - 'reptile from Lu-feng' - was first found in 1930 and was one of the most complete dinosaurs found in China up until then. It came from Upper Triassic rocks of about 200 mya in Yunnan Province in the south west.

Lufengosaurus huenei is a member of the family of prosauropod dinosaurs, a group which lived in the late Triassic and early Jurassic and had a worldwide distribution. They appear to be the first dinosaurs to exploit plant food and may well have eaten meat as well. It was about 20ft/6m long, probably moved on all fours for some of the time and could easily have stood on its hind legs to reach tree top foliage. It was related to the European *Plateosaurus*.

The Chinese have many 'firsts' in science and technology, with *Lufengosaurus* they have a philatelic first by issuing **THE FIRST STAMP FEATURING A DINOSAUR.**

Pl.23

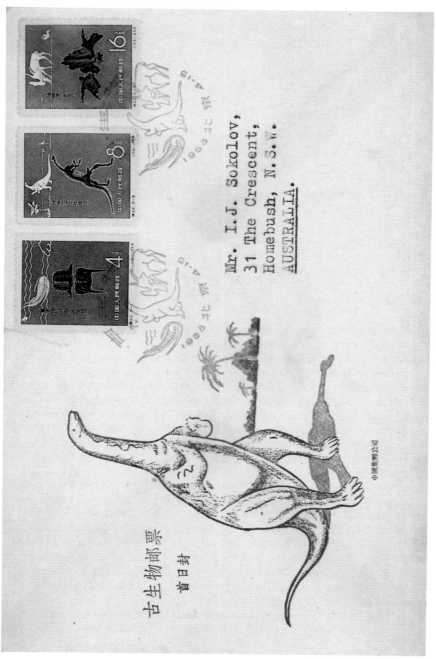

A rare first day cover featuring *Lufengosaurus* and showing the other two stamps in the set: a trilobite, *Kaolishania*, from Hao Li Shan and a deer, *Sinomegaceros*. All three animals appear on the cancellation. From the Peter H. von Bitter collection.

Pl.24   40

CONGO (Brazzaville)
PREHISTORIC ANIMALS. 1970.

Kentrosaurus

Brachiosaurus

Kentrosaurus - 'prickly reptile', is a small stegosaurid dinosaur about 8.2ft/2.5m long from the late Jurassic of Tanzania of about 145 mya. It had a very distinctive pattern of defensive spikes - those on the head and front of the body are plate-like and flat, whilst those further back and on the tail are progressively sharper and narrower. It was contemporary with *Stegosaurus*.

PREHISTORIC ANIMALS. 1975.

Moschops   Stegosaurus

Moschops - 'calf face', was a large plant-eating mammal-like reptile from the late Permian Karoo Beds of South Africa of about 250 mya. It was about 16ft/5m long with a large massive head and a deep body. Its forehead bones were very thick, suggesting that it engaged in head-butting contests. It belongs to a group appropriately called dinocephalians meaning 'terrible heads'.

Tyrannosaurus   Cryptoclidus

Cryptoclidus - 'hidden key', a long-necked plesiosaur ('near reptile') from the late Jurassic of England of about 145 mya. The plesiosaurs were large carnivorous sea reptiles up to 46ft/14m long with the limbs modified to form long paddles. *Cryptoclidus*, about 13ft/4m in length, had jaws with many sharp curved teeth.

CUBA
BACONAO NATIONAL PARK PREHISTORIC ANIMALS
(1st Series). 1985.

Pteranodon   *Monoclonius*

Monoclonius - 'single shoot', a short-frilled horned dinosaur from the late Cretaceous of North America of about 78 mya. It is often confused with *Centrosaurus* 'sharp point reptile', and was about 20ft/6m long.

<u>*Apatosaurus*</u>   *Iguanodon_*

_*Stegosaur<u>us</u>*   *Corythosaurus*

This set is from the Simon Kelly Collection.

CUBA

BACONAO NATIONAL PARK PREHISTORIC ANIMALS (1st Series).
1985.

Tyrannosaurus

BACONAO NATIONAL PARK PREHISTORIC ANIMALS (2nd Series).

1987.

Triceratops

Pelycosaur

Euoplocephalus

Styracosaurus

Saurolophus

Tyrannosaurus

Pl.27

DAHOMEY   PREHISTORIC ANIMALS. 1978.

DHUFAR   PREHISTORIC ANIMALS. 1980

Rhamphorhynchus

Iguanodon

Dimetrodon

Saltoposuchus - 'forest-crocodile', a lightly-built thecodont ('socket teeth') about 3.75ft/1.3m long from the late Triassic of Europe of about 210 mya. The thecodonts were ancestral to the dinosaurs, pterosaurs and crocodiles. From the Stephen King collection.

Archaeopteryx

Pl.28   44

EQUATORIAL GUINEA
PREHISTORIC ANIMALS. 1978.

*Dimetrodon_*

Stegosaurus

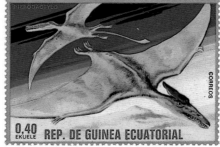

*Rhamphorhynchus
& Pteranodon*

Corythosaurus

Ankylosaurus

Styracosaurus

Triceratops

EQUATORIAL GUINEA
PREHISTORIC ANIMALS. 1978.

Diplodocus - 'double beam' a crude illustration of this medium-sized sauropod from the late Jurassic of North America of about 145 mya. At about 88.5ft/27m but weighing only 10-11 tonnes it was longer, but lighter than *Apatosaurus*.

Plesiosaur - 'near reptile', a poor illustration of a short-necked carnivorous marine reptile belonging to a group called pliosaurs ('more reptile'). These lived in the late Jurassic - early Cretaceous and had paddles for propulsion.

Pl.30   46

Edaphosaurus

Triceratops

Plateosaurus - 'flat reptile', was a European late Triassic - early Jurassic prosauropod dinosaur from about 200 mya. At up to 26ft/8m long, it was the first large dinosaur, and probably ate both plants and meat.

Stegosaurus

Allosaurus

FUJEIRA
MAMMALS AND PREHISTORIC ANIMALS. 1972.

Triceratops

Edaphosaurus

Stegosaurus

Apatosaurus

Triceratops head, upper left

Pl.32   48

GERMANY (EAST)

FOSSILS IN PALAEONTOLOGICAL COLLECTION - BERLIN NATURAL HISTORY MUSEUM. 1973.

Pterodactylus

Archaeopteryx

Pterodactylus - 'wing finger', was a pterosaur or flying reptile and a member of the ruling reptiles or archosaurs, a group which also included the dinosaurs and crocodiles. The pterosaurs were the first successful flying vertebrates and were contemporary with the dinosaurs. Their remains have mainly been found in marine deposits. *Pterodactylus kochi* was small (wingspan about 2ft 5in/75cm), with a long neck and short tail. The hand bones were greatly elongated, in particular the fourth fingers which helped to support the wings. It had long narrow jaws with sharp teeth adapted for a fish diet. *Pterodactylus* has been found in Upper Jurassic rocks of Tanzania and Europe of about 140 mya.

Archaeopteryx - 'ancient wing', is a particularly important fossil as until recently it was the earliest-known bird. The first specimen was found in Germany in 1861 in Upper Jurassic rocks of about 150 mya and is now in the Natural History Museum in London. The specimen shown here is almost complete and was the second to be found in 1877. At 14in/35cm it was about the size of a modern crow and it had a remarkable mixture of bird and reptilian characteristics. Bird-like characters include feathers and a wishbone, reptile-like characters are teeth in the jaws, three claws in each wing and a long bony tail.
An announcement has just been made (June 1991) of two bird-like skeletons discovered in Texas from about 225 mya. It has been named *Protoavis texensis*, 'first bird from Texas' and was about the size of a pheasant. This report if verified means that birds evolved some 75 million years earlier than previously thought and is of great significance.

Pl.33

GERMANY (EAST)
CENTENARY OF NATURAL HISTORY MUSEUM
OF THE HUMBOLDT UNIVERSITY, BERLIN. 1990.

Dicraeosaurus   *Ken͟trosaurus*

Dicraeosaurus - 'forked reptile', was a relatively small sauropod dinosaur from the late Jurassic of Tendaguru (Tanzania) of about 145 mya. It was related to the familiar *Diplodocus* and was described in 1929 on the basis of an almost complete skeleton (41ft/12.6m long) which was collected by an expedition from the Berlin Museum of Natural History in 1908-1912, to the then German East Africa. The skull shows typical diplodocid features: the nostrils on the top of the skull, the snout long and broad with weak peg-like teeth in the front and the eyes far back. The neck and tail were short for a sauropod and the spines projecting up from its backbone had a Y shaped fork at the top from which its name is derived. *Kentrosaurus* and *Brachiosaurus* were found in the same rocks.

Brachiosaurus   *Brachiosaurus*

Brachiosaurus - 'arm reptile', is so named as its front legs are considerably longer than its hind legs, an unusual feature for a sauropod dinosaur. Its shoulders were some 21ft/6.4m from the ground and its humerus or upper arm bone provided about 7ft/2.1m of this. Its neck took up about half its height of 41ft/12.6m and it seems to have been the giraffe equivalent of the dinosaur world. The two stamps here show the skeleton in the Natural History Museum in Berlin, the largest mounted complete dinosaur skeleton in existence, and details of the skull with a reconstruction of its appearance in life.

Pl.34   50

GERMANY (EAST)

CENTENARY OF NATURAL HISTORY MUSEUM
OF THE HUMBOLDT UNIVERSITY, BERLIN. 1990.

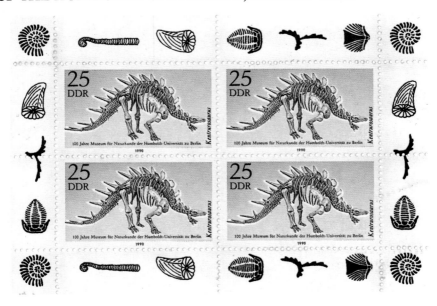

A *se-tenant* block of four *Kentrosaurus* with a border showing various marine invertebrate fossils: ammonites both typical and heteromorph (uncoiled), horn corals, trilobites, graptolites and brachiopods.

Dryosaurus -'oak reptile', belongs to a family of small-to-medium sized ornithopod plant eating dinosaurs called hypsilophodontids (high-ridged teeth). It measured about 10-13ft/3-4m long and was first found in the late Jurassic of western North America of about 145 mya. A specimen from Tanzania was originally described under the name *Dysalotosaurus* ('lost wood reptile') but following a recent bone by bone comparison with *Dryosaurus* it has now been included in that genus and given the specific name *Dryosaurus lettowvorbecki* after a famous German General.

51   Pl.35

GERMANY (EAST)

CENTENARY OF NATURAL HISTORY MUSEUM
OF THE HUMBOLDT UNIVERSITY, BERLIN. 1990.

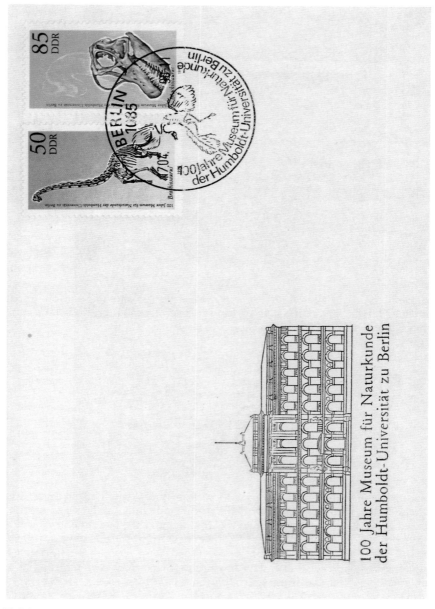

A first day cover with an *Archaeopteryx* cancellation.

Pl.36   52

GRENADA
WALT DISNEY'S FANTASIA. 1991.

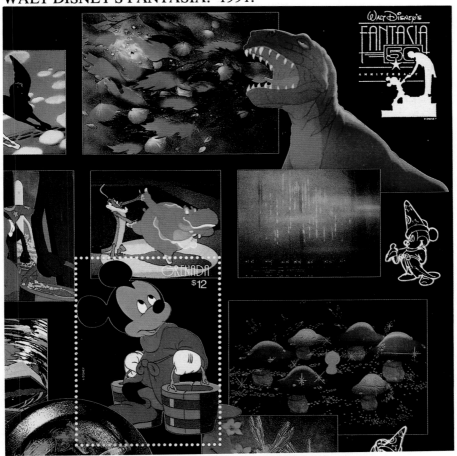

Tyrannosaurus

Pteranodon - 'winged and toothless'. These pterodactytls (more correctly pterosaurs) clearly show the long bony backwards-projecting crest at the back of the skull typical of the late Cretaceous pterosaur ***Pteranodon***.

Pl.37

GUINEA
PREHISTORIC ANIMALS. 1987.

Dimetrodon

Iguanodon

Stegosaurus

Tylosaurus

Pl.38

54

GUINEA

PREHISTORIC ANIMALS. 1987.

This *Triceratops* mini-sheet has an unusually rich reptilian border. Starting at the upper left is a prosauropod-like dinosaur, probably *Plateosaurus*, next clockwise and eating, is an *Allosaurus* with a *Stegosaurus* completing this corner. In the top right are two *Pteranodon* flying. The right is dominated by a *Tyrannosaurus* with an *Anatosaurus* to its left, a herd of three *Ornithomimus* ('bird mimic') is fleeing in the background and in the right foreground is the armoured dinosaur *Euoplocephalus*, formerly called *Scolosaurus*. The centre bottom is filled by the large brontosaur *Apatosaurus*, to its left in the bottom corner is the small dinosaur *Ornitholestes* ('bird robber') and completing the border on the left is the pelycosaur *Dimetrodon*. This gives a total on this mini-sheet of ten different dinosaurs, one pterosaur and one pelycosaur. The illustrations are from paintings by different artists including Z. Burian and the American Rudolph Zallinger.

                                                                    Pl.39

GUINEA - BISSAU

PREHISTORIC ANIMALS. 1989.

Anatosaurus

Mesosaurus

Tyrannosaurus

Stegosaurus

Edaphosaurus

The illustrations in this set are all from paintings by the artist Z. Burian.

Pl.40   56

HUNGARY   MINERALS & FOSSILS.
CENTENARY OF THE HUNGARIAN GEOLOGICAL INSTITUTE.
1969.

Placochelys - 'flat turtle', was about 3ft/90 cm long and belongs to a group of mid-to-late Triassic central European marine reptiles called Placodonts ('flat teeth') from about 225 mya. Though turtle-like in appearance, an example of convergent evolution, they were not turtles. The body was armour-plated and the skull had short powerful jaws with teeth adapted for culling and eating shellfish.

PREHISTORIC ANIMALS. 1990.

Tarbosaurus - 'alarming reptile', is a late Cretaceous large (up to 46ft/14m long) bipedal carnivorous dinosaur from the Nemegt Basin, Gobi Desert, Mongolia of about 67 mya. It was closely related to and very like *Tyrannosaurus*, and is included in this genus by some authorities.
Dimorphodon - 'two-form tooth', is an early Jurassic pterosaur from southern England of about 195 mya. It had a wingspan about 4ft/1.2m, a strong beak and jaw with long teeth in the front and many smaller ones at the back..

HUNGARY
PREHISTORIC ANIMALS. 1990.

First day covers from the Mike Howgate collection.   *Stegosaurus*

Pl.42   58

HUNGARY
INTERNATIONAL LITERARY YEAR. 1990.

Dinosaurs reading

The green dinosaur on the left is reading a newspaper, possibly the "Dinosaur Times", with a picture of dinosaurs on the front cover. The red dinosaur on the right is reading a book appropriately titled "The saurus Lexikon".

JAPAN
CENTENARY OF NATIONAL SCIENCE MUSEUM. 1977.

The National Science Museum in Tokyo is concerned with the history of nature and natural science. The 50 yen stamp shows the museum, a constellation and a long-necked plesiosaur ('near reptile') *Wellesisaurus* 'Welles's reptile'. The plesiosaurs were carnivorous Mesozoic marine reptiles with large paddles designed for underwater 'flying' as in modern penguins. Dean Conybeare, a 19th century palaeontologist, described these reptiles as 'snakes threaded through the bodies of turtles'.

JAPAN
CENTENARY OF NATIONAL SCIENCE MUSEUM. 1977.

First day cover.

Pl.44
60

KAMPUCHEA
PREHISTORIC ANIMALS. 1986.

Edaphosaurus

Sauroctonus - 'reptile killer', a carnivorous therapsid (mammal-like reptile) from the Permian of eastern Europe of about 250 mya. The therapsids are thought to have descended from the Pelycosaurs, most were about 3ft 3in/1m long and include both herbivores and carnivores. *Sauroctonus* belonged to a group called gorgonopsians who were the dominant land predators in southern Africa and eastern Europe at this time.

Mastodonsaurus - 'breast-shaped tooth reptile', a large (up to 10ft/3m long) carnivorous labyrinthodont amphibian from the Triassic of Europe of about 230 mya. The group name comes from the infolding of the enamel of the teeth into a labryinthine structure. It belongs to the temnospondyl ('split vertebrae') group which ranged from the early Carboniferous to the early Jurassic and which gave rise to the ancestors of our modern frogs and toads.

KAMPUCHEA

PREHISTORIC ANIMALS. 1986.

Early illustrations of *Brachiosaurus* such as this show it in relatively deep water. One authority has calculated that if it were submerged to its full depth the water pressure would be sufficient to collapse its lungs, suggesting that such illustrations are now incorrect.

Rhamphorhynchus

Tarbosaurus

Brachiosaurus

Pl.46   62

KOREA (NORTH)
CONQUERORS OF THE UNIVERSE. 1980.

The 30ch stamp shows a *Stegosaurus* (left), a human astride a dinosaur - the flat head suggests it could be an ankylosaur, and a pterosaur in the sky.
The 40ch stamp shows a carnivorous dinosaur, probably *Tyrannosaurus*, being prodded by a human. The title of the set is perhaps a little over ambitious.

KUWAIT
TENTH ANNIVERSARY OF SCIENCE AND
NATURAL HISTORY MUSEUM. 1982.

The dinosaur shown here is probably the prosauropod *Plateosaurus* 'flat reptile', from about 200 mya. The prosauropods had a worldwide distribution, were the first large dinosaurs and appear to be the earliest plant-eating dinosaurs though they may have been meat-eaters as well. They lived during the late Triassic and early Jurassic. *Plateosaurus* was up to 26ft/8m long, and could walk on all fours or on its hind limbs only.

LAOS
PREHISTORIC ANIMALS. 1988.

Anatosaurus

Tyrannosaurus

These two illustrations are both from the same Z.Burian painting of 1938 and are shown in their relative positions. The names on the stamps have been transposed in error and as explained in the Aden set the correct name for the hadrosaurian dinosaur is **Anatosaurus** and not **Trachodon** as shown.

Iguanodon

Euoplocephalus

The **Iguanodon** is from a 1941 Burian painting and the **Euoplocephalus** 'true plated head' is from a 1955 Burian painting. In the latter an attacking **Albertosaurus** has been removed for the stamp. **Euoplocephalus** was a heavily armoured dinosaur about 20ft/6m long from the late Cretaceous of North America and Asia of about 85 mya. The tail had a heavy bony club at the end.

Pl.48   64

LAOS
PREHISTORIC ANIMALS. 1988.

The dinosaur *Ceratosaurus*
taken from an 1941 Z. Burian painting.

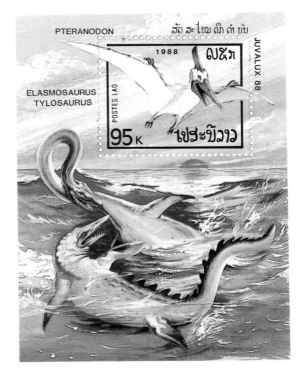

Elasmosaurus - 'plated reptile', was a late Cretaceous long-necked plesiosaur from Japan and Kansas, U.S.A. of about 70 mya. At 46ft/14m with some 26ft/8m of neck it was the longest-known plesiosaur. It has been suggested that it paddled on the surface of the sea with the head held high in the air enabling it to spot prey easily in the water below. It is shown with the mosasaur *Tylosaurus* and the pterosaur *Pteranodon* and is from a Z. Burian painting.

LAOS
PREHISTORIC ANIMALS. 1988.

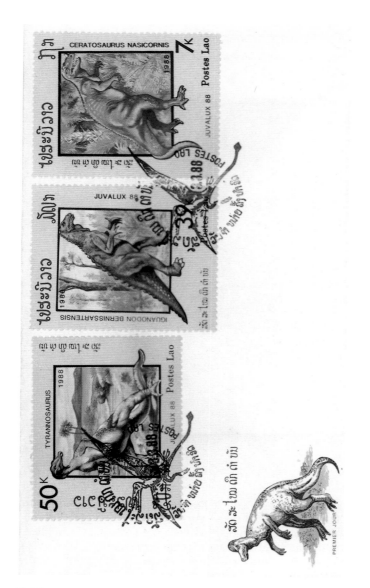

A first day cover featuring the late Cretaceous crested hadrosaurian dinosaur *Corythosaurus* taken from a 1955 Burian painting, with the late Jurassic pterosaur *Rhamphorhynchus* used as a frank. From the Andrew Scott collection.

Pl.50

66

LESOTHO
FOOTPRINTS OF PREHISTORIC REPTILES (1st Series). 1970.

Fossilized reptile footprints occur in great variety and abundance at Moyeni in the Quthing district of Lesotho in upper Triassic rocks of about 200 mya. The 3c stamp shows tracks made by various different reptiles and impressions of trailing tails, one of which shows that an animal moved from water to shore. The other stamps in the set show tracks in the foreground with an indication in the background of the type of reptile which could have made them.

Gryponyx   *Plateosauravus*

Gryponyx - 'curved claw', is generally regarded as a prosauropod dinosaur though its generic name is dubious. It was a long slender bipedal animal about 14.5ft/4.5m long with sharp pointed teeth.

Plateosauravus - 'flat reptile grandfather' was a prosauropod dinosaur similar to but at 10-13ft/3-4m long, rather smaller than *Plateosaurus*. It had four toes on its broad hind feet and much smaller fore legs and could walk on all fours or on its hind limbs only. The tracks show prints of both fore and hind feet.

Tritylodon   *Massospondylus*

Tritylodon - 'trident tooth', was not a dinosaur but a plant-eating mammal-like reptile with a very specialized dentition. The Tritylodonts were a very successful group with skull sizes ranging from 3-8.6in/8-22cm.

Massospondylus - 'massive vertebrae', was another prosauropod dinosaur which has also been found in Asia. It was somewhat smaller than *Plateosaurus*, and was probably a high browser, feeding on vegetation out of reach of other animals.

LESOTHO
FOOTPRINTS OF PREHISTORIC REPTILES (1st Series). 1970.

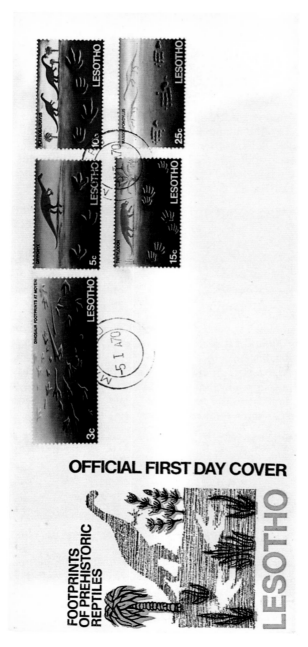

A first day cover featuring a typical prosauropod dinosaur. From the Peter H. von Bitter collection.

Pl.52

LESOTHO

FOOTPRINTS OF PREHISTORIC REPTILES (2nd Series). 1984.

The **sauropodomorphs** are the group that includes the giant quadrupeds, undoubtedly the most spectacular of all the dinosaurs because of their size. Some of the more familiar names in this group are: *Apatosaurus*, *Brachiosaurus*, *Diplodocus*, *'Supersaurus'* and *'Ultrasaurus'*.

Lesothosaurus - 'Lesotho reptile', was a small 35in/90cm long, lightly-built bipedal herbivorous dinosaur which probably avoided predators by running fast on long slender hind legs. The small leaf-shaped teeth were suitable for breaking food into small pieces rather than for chewing.

Carnivorous dinosaurs are all bipedal theropods (beast-feet) and have long sharp claws on their hind feet. These leave characteristic tracks or prints which can usually be distinguished from those made by the herbivorous sauropodomorphs and ornithischian (bird-hipped) dinosaurs.

This set is from the Geology Department, National Museum of Wales, collection.

MALAGASY
PREHISTORIC ANIMALS. 1988.

Tyrannosaurus

Stegosaurus

Triceratops

Saurolophus - 'ridged reptile', from the late Cretaceous of North America and Mongolia of about 68 mya, was a duck-billed dinosaur about 30ft/9m long with a solid bony spike at the back of its skull. From the Robert M. Owens collection.

Pl.54   70

MALDIVES
PREHISTORIC ANIMALS. 1972.

Stegosaurus

Dimetrodon

Diplodocus

Triceratops

Pteranodon

Tyrannosaurus

The illustration on the 5R stamp is by Rudolph Zallinger and is taken from the famous mural in the Peabody Museum at Yale University in the United States.

Pl.55   71

MALI

PREHISTORIC ANIMALS. 1984.

Dimetrodon

Dimetrodon

Iguanodon

Iguanodon

Archaeopteryx

Archaeopteryx

Triceratops

This set is from the Mike Howgate collection.

Pl.56   72

MANAMAR
PREHISTORIC ANIMALS. 1972.

Stegosaurus

Plateosaurus

Styracosaurus

Allosaurus

73

Pl.57

MANAMAR

PREHISTORIC ANIMALS. 1972.

Apatosaurus

Pteranodon

Dimetrodon

Allosaurus

Pl.58

74

MONGOLIA

PREHISTORIC ANIMALS. 1966.

Tarbosaurus

Talarurus

Talarurus - 'basket tail', is an ankylosaurid (fused reptile), a specialized group of dinosaurs with broad armoured heads, horns at the rear corners of the skull, an armour-plated body and a tail modified into a bony club. It comes from the late Cretaceous of southern Mongolia of about 78 mya, and measures about 16-23ft/5-7m long.

Protoceratops

Saurolophus

Pl.59

MONGOLIA

PREHISTORIC ANIMALS. 1977.

Psittacosaurus

Mongolemys

Mongolemys - 'Mongolian fresh-water turtle', a late Cretaceous Turtle from the Nemegt area in the Gobi Desert, Mongolia of about 67 mya. Its carapace or shell was about 8in/20cm long and came from sediments indicating a brackish to fresh water lakeside environment. This is the only Mesozoic chelonian shown on a stamp to date and was first described in 1971.

Psittacosaurus - 'parrot reptile', is an early-to-late Cretaceous ceratopian (horn-faced) bipedal plant-eating dinosaur from Mongolia of about 95 mya. It was a lightly-built animal about 6ft 6in/2m long with a curved parrot-like beak from which its name is derived.

This set it from the Geology Department, National Museum of Wales, and Robert M. Owens collections.

PREHISTORIC ANIMALS. 1990.

Chasmosaurus   *Stegosaurus*

Chasmosaurus 'ravine reptile', a late Cretaceous quadrupedal ceratopian plant-eating dinosaur from western North America of about 75 mya. Abundant remains have been found in the Red Deer River Valley, Alberta, Canada. It was about 16ft/5m long, had three facial horns and an unusual long frill at the rear of its skull with large bony openings and a square-shaped back.

Pl.60   76

MONGOLIA

PREHISTORIC ANIMALS. 1990.

Probactrosaurus

Opisthocoelicaudia.

Probactrosaurus - 'before the Bactrian reptile', was an Iguanodontid plant-eating ornithopod dinosaur some 20ft/6m long, from the early Cretaceous of eastern Asia of about 105 mya. Anatomically it had several hadrosaurian features and it may have been close to the ancestor of the duckbills.

Opisthocoelicaudia - 'posterior cavity tail', was a sauropod dinosaur with a relatively short neck and tail from the late Cretaceous of Mongolia of about 70 mya. Its length has been estimated to be about 39ft/12m and its name is derived from the concavity in the rear of each of the tail vertebrae, which is opposite to that found in most sauropods.

Tarbosaurus

Iguanodon

MONGOLIA

PREHISTORIC ANIMALS. 1990.

Mamenchisaurus - 'Mamenchi reptile', is a very long sauropod dinosaur similar in many ways to *Diplodocus*, and comes from the late Jurassic of Sichuan Province, China of about 145 mya. Its total length was some 72ft/22m of which the exceptionally long neck took up 33ft/10m, making it the longest neck of any known animal. No complete skeletons have so far been found, but reconstructions have been made based on remains from several animals. The long neck must have given it a considerable feeding advantage, particularly when it was on its hind legs, as it would have been able to reach far higher foliage than other dinosaurs. The illustration is taken from a 1986 Mark Hallett painting.

A herd of *Brachiosaurus* being attacked by an *Allosaurus*, from a John Gurche painting.

Pl.62

MONGOLIA
THE FLINTSTONES. 1991.

To Flintstones fans 'Dino' the dinosaur needs no introduction. Though his affinities
are uncertain, he appears to be descended from a sauropodomorph with stegosaurian
affinities that survived the great extinction at the end of the Cretaceous.

MONGOLIA

THE FLINTSTONES. 1991.

Pl.64   80

MOROCCO

DINOSAUR OF TILOUGGUITE. 1988.

Cetiosaurus - 'whale reptile', was another of the large sauropod dinosaurs. The earliest descriptions were based on various incomplete remains, the first of which were found in Oxfordshire in 1809. In 1979 at Tilougguite in Morocco, a fairly complete skeleton was discovered giving a much better idea of its size and shape. The thigh bones measured over 6ft/1.8m and one of the shoulder blades was over 5ft/1.5m long. It lived in the late Jurassic about 145 mya, was up to 60ft/18.3m long and may have weighed as much as 9 tonnes.

PREMIER JOUR D'ÉMISSION
———
FIRST DAY COVER

MOROCCAN MASONIC HISTORY

This former French colony has an interesting Masonic history. The irregular Grand Orient of France formed five lodges there, beginning in 1891. Subsequently the Grand Lodge of France and the Grand Orient of Italy erected Lodges in the country. In 1902, Lodge Coronation No. 934 was established with a Scottish warrant, and England chartered New Friendship Lodge No. 4997 in 1927. Both these lodges started their lives at Tangier, but both soon moved to Gibraltar. New Friendship Lodge subsequently changed its name to Gibraltar Lodge. Moroccan Independence in 1956 would appear to have not been condusive to tranquil Masonic development. Nonetheless, the Grand Lodge 'Atlas' of Morocco was erected at Casablanca in 1967. It was formed by three Lodges then under the Grand Lodge of Switzerland.

MOZAMBIQUE
ROCKS, MINERALS AND FOSSILS. 1971.

Endothiodon - 'inside beast tooth', was a plant-eating mammal-like reptile or Therapsid, from the late Permian of south and east Africa of about 250 mya. It belongs to a group called dicynodonts ('two dog teeth') and was about 8ft 3in/2.5m long.

NICARAGUA
PREHISTORIC ANIMALS. 1987.

Triceratops

Dimetrodon

Pteranodon

Tylosaurus

Pl.66   82

NIGER   ARCHAEOLOGY. 1976.

Ouranosaurus - 'brave reptile', was a medium-sized (23ft/7m long), ornithopod dinosaur from lower Cretaceous sediments in Niger, dating from about 108 mya, which indicated that it lived in a dry equatorial climate. It was remarkable for the 'sail' on its back reaching from its shoulders to half way down its tail, which was supported by elongated spines along its backbone.

OMAN
PREHISTORIC ANIMALS. 1980

Diploceraspis - 'two horned shield', was a newt-like amphibian 3ft/90cm long, from the early Permian of North Africa of about 275 mya with a most unusual horned skull. *Cynognathus* - 'dog jaw', was a powerful carnivorous cynodont ('dog teeth'), mammal-like reptile from the early Triassic of South Africa and South America of about 240 mya, and was some 3ft 3in/1m long. This set is from the Stephen King collection.

POLAND PREHISTORIC ANIMALS (1st Series). 1965.

Pl.68

POLAND
PREHISTORIC ANIMALS (1st Series). 1965.

PREHISTORIC ANIMALS (2nd Series). 1966.

POLAND
FIRST DAY COVERS (Reduced). 1965-1966.

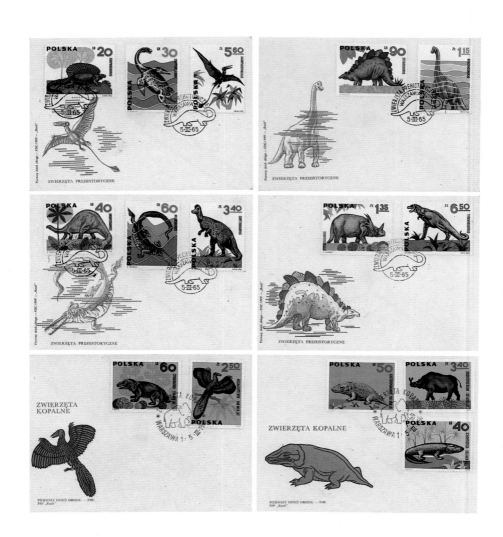

Pl.70

86

POLAND
POLISH SCIENTIFIC EXPEDITIONS. 1980.

Palaeontology,
Mongolia

The large fossil skeleton shown here is unnamed but following the precepts laid down by one Sherlock Holmes, it should be possible to make a few elementary deductions. **Holmes:** "Its size and shape indicate that it is most likely to be a land animal, from this it could be deduced to be either a mammal or a reptile. Close examination of the skull reveals the presence of two openings in the skull behind the eye suggesting that it is a diapsid reptile and hence not a mammal. The teeth appear to be long, dagger-like and pointed, indicating a carnivorous dinosaur. It is known that the Polish Mongolian Expedition excavated a skeleton of the carnivorous dinosaur ***Tarbosaurus bataar*** ('alarming reptile from Bataar') during their 1970 season, hence my dear Watson I would proffer this as my provisional diagnosis!"
Watson: "Holmes, you astound me, your diagnosis has my **'stamp'** of approval."

RUSSIA
PREHISTORIC ANIMALS. 1990.

Sordes

Saurolophus

Sordes pilosus - 'hairy devil', was a late Jurassic pterosaur from Kazakhstan in central Asia of about 140 mya with a wingspan of 1ft 6in/50cm. Palaeontologists have long argued about whether dinosaurs and pterosaurs were warm-blooded. If they were then an insulating layer of fur would provide positive evidence for this hypothesis. In 1970, *Sordes* was found in fine-grained sediments containing impressions of a possible body fur, though this evidence is not accepted by all palaeontologists.

Pl.71

ST. THOMAS AND PRINCE
PREHISTORIC ANIMALS. 1982.

Parasaurolophus   *Stegosaurus*

Parasaurolophus - 'beside ridged reptile', had the most striking head-crest of all the hadrosaurid or duck-billed dinosaurs. It was basically a long hollow tube up to 6ft/1.8m long that extended beyond the back of the skull by some 3ft 3in/1m. It has been suggested that the crest may have been used as a deflector of branches when it was running through dense undergrowth. As it contained a pair of nasal passages it could also have acted as a resonator in producing a unique call for social communication. *Parasaurolophus* lived in the late Cretaceous of North America about 72 mya and was about 33ft/10m long.

Triceratops   *Tyrannosaurus rex*

Apatosaurus   *Dimetrodon*

Pl.72   88

ST. THOMAS AND PRINCE
PREHISTORIC ANIMALS. 1982.

Pteranodon

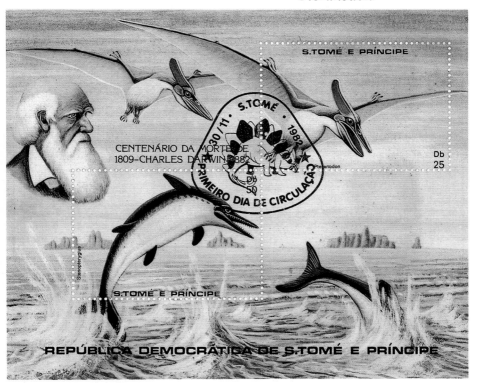

Stenopterygius

A mini-sheet commemorating the centenary of the death of Charles Darwin, 1809-1882, with a *Stegosaurus* cancellation.

Stenopterygius - 'narrow fins', was an Ichthyosaur ('fish lizard'), a group of carnivorous reptiles that had become completely adapted to life in the sea. Its ecology and shape were similar to that of our modern dolphins, an example of convergent evolution. It comes from the early to middle Jurassic, about 190-170 mya, of England and Germany and measured up to 10ft/3m long. Its paddles were long and narrow in contrast to those in *Ichthyosaurus* which were short and broad. In Germany, adult skeletons have been found with baby skeletons inside, indicating that they gave birth to live young at sea.

Pl.73

ST. THOMAS AND PRINCE

PREHISTORIC ANIMALS. 1982. Two of six first day cards

Pl.74

90

ST. VINCENT
THE FLINTSTONES. 1990.

Pl.75

ST. VINCENT

THE FLINTSTONES. 1990.

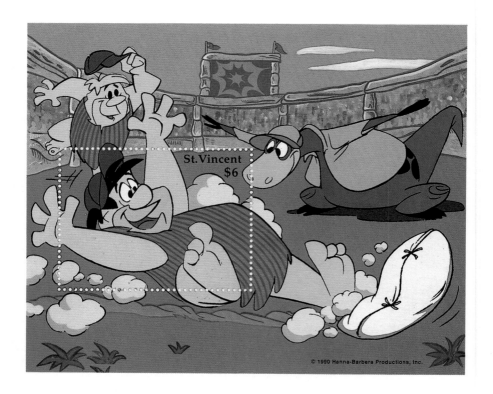

Pl.76   92

SAN MARINO
PREHISTORIC ANIMALS. 1965.

Apatosaurus

Pteranodon
Brachiosaurus

Brachiosaurus - 'arm reptile', has front legs considerably longer than its hind legs.
This illustration is incorrect in this respect.

Elasmosaurus

Stegosaurus

Tyrannosaurus

Iguanodon

Thaumatosaurus

Triceratops

Thaumatosaurus - 'wonderful reptile', was a carnivorous marine reptile belonging
to the group of long-necked plesiosaurs. It comes from the early to middle Jurassic
of Europe of about 190-170 mya. It was related to *Elasmosaurus* also shown in
this set, but was smaller and had a shorter neck.

Pl.77

SAN MARINO

PREHISTORIC ANIMALS. 1965.

A first day cover featuring *Tyrannosaurus* from the Peter H. von Bitter collection.

Pl.78   94

SOUTH AFRICA   KAROO FOSSILS. 1982.

A fine *se-tenant* block of four mini-sheet with a border featuring *Lesothosaurus* 'reptile from Lesotho', an early Jurassic ornithopod dinosaur about 35in/90cm long. The four stamps are also available separately but as they do not differ they are not repeated here. *Lystrosaurus* has been described earlier. About half the surface of the Republic of South Africa is covered by rocks of the Karoo Sequence dating from the Permian and Triassic about 250 to 150 mya. Abundant fossils provide an excellent record of the evolution of land animals during this time.

Bradysaurus - 'slow reptile' on the 8c stamp, was a large sluggish herbivorous stem-reptile from the middle Permian of about 250 mya. It was about 16ft/5m long, had a thick body and short legs. Its teeth suggest a diet of soft water plants.

Euparkeria - 'Parker's true animal' (20c stamp), was a small, agile bipedal carnivorous reptile up to 2ft/20cm long from the early Triassic of about 220 mya. It belongs to the Ornithosuchia ('bird crocodiles'), a group generally thought to be ancestral to the dinosaurs.

Thrinaxodon - 'three ridged tooth' on the 25c stamp, was a small, carnivorous mongoose-like cynodont reptile from the early Triassic of about 220 mya. It was about 20in/50cm long, had many mammalian characteristics and could have been ancestral to the mammals.

SOUTH AFRICA

KAROO FOSSILS. 1982. Commemorative covers (Reduced).

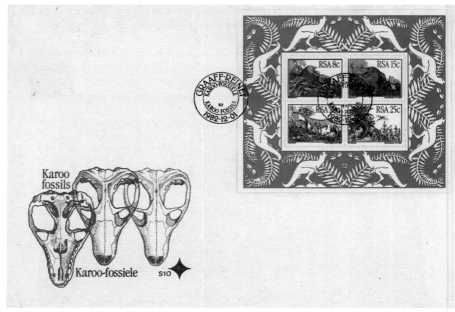

The large first day cover features *Emydops* 'tortoise face'. This was a dicynodont herbivorous reptile about the size of a rabbit with a long body and short stumpy legs. Its name is derived from the horny covering on the tips of its jaws as in tortoises. It lived in the late Permian about 250 mya.

The small first day cover features *Heterodontosaurus* 'mixed tooth reptile'. This was a small two-legged plant-eating dinosaur up to about 4ft 11in/1.5m long from the lower Jurassic of about 185 mya. It had three kinds of teeth - cutting teeth in front of the upper jaw, two pairs of canine-like teeth and grinding cheek teeth. This cover is from the Peter H. von Bitter collection.

Pl.80   96

TANZANIA
PREHISTORIC AND MODERN ANIMALS. 1988.

Plateosaurus

Pteranodon

Apatosaurus

Stegosaurus

PREHISTORIC ANIMALS. 1991.

Pl.81

TANZANIA
PREHISTORIC ANIMALS. 1991.

Edmontosaurus - 'reptile from Edmonton', a large (33-42ft/10-13m) hadrosaurid dinosaur from the late Cretaceous of North America of about 67 mya.

Pl.82

98

TANZANIA
PREHISTORIC ANIMALS. 1991.

Silvisaurus - 'forest reptile' belongs to the group of armoured dinosaurs called nodosaurids ('nodular reptiles'). It lived in the early Cretaceous of North America of about 95 mya and measured some 11ft/3.4m long. It had heavy nodular bony armour and flank spikes on its neck and body.

Silvisaurus

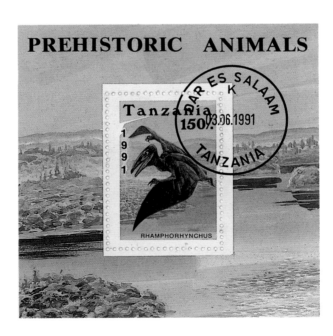

Pl.83

TONGA
THE EVOLUTION OF THE EARTH. 1989.

The T$1 stamp shows a fish and its fossil looking like *Eusthenopteron* ('strong fin'), an amphibian resembling *Ichthyostega* and a dragonfly - possibly *Meganeura*. Though the stamp is called Carboniferous, the two vertebrates are from the late Devonian. The other two values show skeletal remains and reconstructions, with the T$2 stamp also picturing two early mammals.

TURKS AND CAICOS
EXTINCT ANIMALS. 1990

Mesosaurus

Pl.84   100

TONGA
THE EVOLUTION OF THE EARTH. 1989.

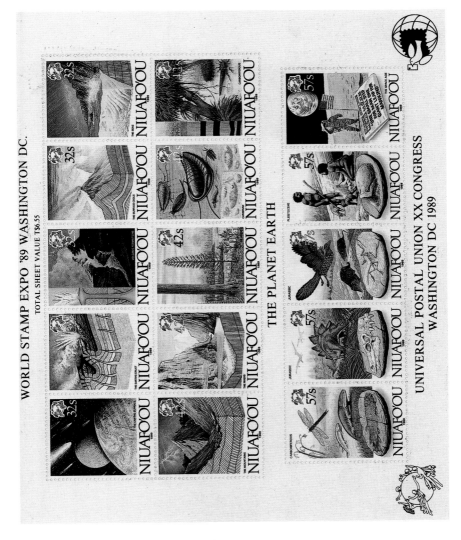

Evolution of the Earth, 1989.
This magnificently-coloured sheet shows a few events in the history of the earth up to the first landing of man on the moon. It if is intended to be in sequence, it is a pity that the trees and land plants in the centre stamp were not positioned following the Cambrian, as they first evolved after the Cambrian and before the Carboniferous. Its position may of course have a different significance.

Pl.85

TONGA
THE EVOLUTION OF THE EARTH. 1989.

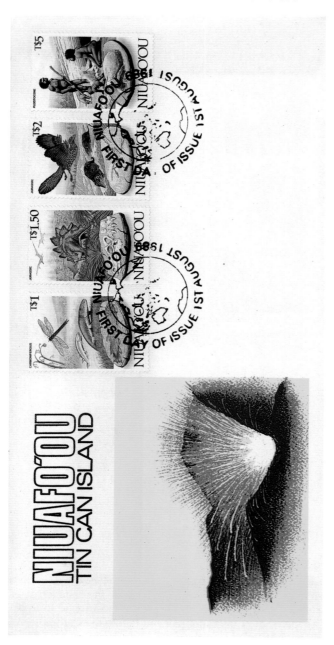

The name Tin Can Island derives from the difficulties ships had in landing in olden times. Mail to be delivered would be placed in sealed tin cans and cast overboard for wind and tide to deliver it to shore.

UNITED STATES OF AMERICA

CENTENARY OF AMERICAN MUSEUM OF NATURAL HISTORY.
1970.

The **Age of Reptiles** stamp is taken from the Jurassic part of the famous mural in the Peabody Museum at Yale University which was painted by Rudolph Zallinger. It shows many familiar reptiles from left to right: *Diplodocus, Apatosaurus, Stegosaurus, Allosaurus, Camptosaurus* and *Compsognathus. Archaeopteryx* and *Rhamphorynchus* are also present. The plants include *Neocalamites, Williamsonia, Matondium, Araucarites, Cycadeoidea, Cycadella,* and *Wielandella.*

UNITED STATES OF AMERICA
PREHISTORIC ANIMALS. 1989.

This *se-tenant* block of four aroused particular interest at the time of issue for two completely different reasons. First; the dinosaur labelled **Brontosaurus** as explained in the Aden set, is correctly called **Apatosaurus**. This error caused a furore amongst the purists and generated a great debate in the popular press. The whole story and the scientific background is told in S.J. Gould's latest book *"Bully for Brontosaurus"*, 1991 and is highly-recommended reading for those wanting to know more. Second; an unknown genius in the United States Postal Service invented the 'Stamposaurus' shown on the margin. This was an outstanding success and must be one of the few cases on record where the margin is now more collectable than the stamps. At the same time many special cancellations were produced throughout the U.S.A. either featuring Stamposaurus or other dinosaurs.

Pl.88   104

VIETNAM
PREHISTORIC ANIMALS. 1979.

Plesiosaurus

Apatosaurus

Plesiosaurus - 'near reptile', a carnivorous marine reptile about 7ft 6in/2.3m long, from the early Jurassic of Europe of about 185 mya. Its structure made it highly manoeuvrable rather than built for speed.

Iguanodon

Tyrannosaurus

Stegosaurus

Mosasaurus

Mosasaurus - 'Meuse reptile', was so named as the first remains were found in 1770 near the river Meuse in Holland. It was a large carnivorous marine lizard from the late Cretaceous of about 70 mya.

Pl.89

VIETNAM
PREHISTORIC ANIMALS. 1979.

Triceratops

Pteranodon

PREHISTORIC ANIMALS. 1984.

Styracosaurus

Diplodocus

Rhamphorhynchus

Corythosaurus

Pl.90

VIETNAM
PREHISTORIC ANIMALS. 1984.

Allosaurus

Seymouria

Seymouria - 'from Seymour, Texas' comes from the early Permian of North America of about 260 mya. It was a labyrinthodont amphibian about 2ft/60cm long, well adapted for life on land, though when first discovered it was thought to be an early reptile.

Dimetrodon   *Brachiosaurus*

PREHISTORIC ANIMALS. 1990.

Albertosaurus   *Ceratosaurus*

Albertosaurus - 'reptile from Alberta', a carnivorous dinosaur from the late Cretaceous of Canada of about 70 mya. It was related to, but at about 29ft 6in/9m long, was much smaller than its contemporary *Tyrannosaurus*. Its most likely prey would have been duckbilled dinosaurs. Most material formerly described as *Gorgosaurus* 'dragon reptile' is now included in the genus *Albertosaurus*.

Ankylosaurus   *Euoplocephalus*

Edaphosaurus

Pl.92   108

YEMEN REPUBLIC

SPACE 70. CONQUEST OF MARS. 1971.

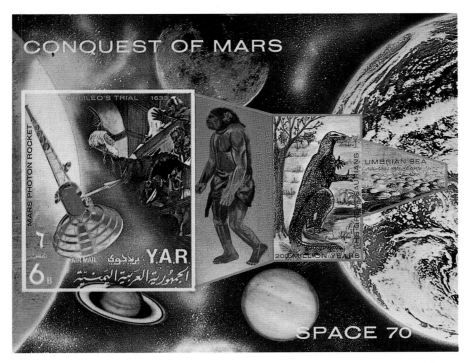

An *Iguanodon* represents the age of Saurians.

PREHISTORIC ANIMALS. 1990.

Edaphosaurus   *Dimorphodon*

YEMEN REPUBLIC

PREHISTORIC ANIMALS. 1990.

Ichthyosaurus - 'fish reptile', the genus from which the Ichthyosaurs take their name. It was an early Jurassic to early Cretaceous carnivorous marine reptile about 6ft 6in/2m long that lived from about 190 to 120 mya in Europe, Greenland and North America. Its remains have been found in great abundance and detail at Holzmaden in Germany, recording births, body shape, stomach contents and fossil droppings. Even the remains of pigment cells have been found indicating that the skin may have been a dark reddish brown.

Pl.94

YUGOSLAVIA
MUSEUM EXHIBITS. FOSSILS. 1985.

Pachyophis - 'thick snake', was actually a lizard that looked like a snake, in the same way that the modern 'glass snake' and European 'slow worm' do. It is regarded as a transitional form between the lizards and snakes and comes from the late Cretaceous of Europe of about 75 mya.

ZAMBIA
ZAMBIAN PREHISTORIC ANIMALS. 1973.

Zambiasaurus - 'reptile from Zambia', was a Therapsid mammal-like reptile belonging to the group called dicynodonts from the Middle Triassic of about 245 mya. It comes from the Luangwa valley whose river is a major tributary of the great Zambezi River. Juvenile remains have been found and enough of an adult to show that it was a large, up to 16ft/3m long herbivore which would have used its large horny beak to crop vegetation.

Pl.95

ZAMBIA

ZAMBIAN PREHISTORIC ANIMALS. 1973.

Oudenodon - 'without teeth', a plant-eating dicynodont being attacked by the carnivorous gorgonopsid 'dragon like', **Rubidgea** 'after Mr S.H. Rubidge', in a late Permian South African scene of about 250 mya. **Rubidgea** had very long upper canine teeth (as in the Pleistocene sabre-toothed cats), and must have been able to open its jaws exceptionally wide to be able to use them for killing. The stamp illustrates the point. Its incisors were probably used to tear chunks off its prey, which would then be swallowed whole. Both the animals shown were therapsids or mammal-like reptiles.

Luangwa - 'after Luangwa valley', was another mammal-like reptile belonging to the mainly carnivorous group called cynodonts 'dog teeth'. It lived in the middle Triassic about 240 mya. The cynodonts were a very successful group of therapsid reptiles living from the late Permian to the middle Jurassic, a period of about 80 million years. They were the group that gave rise to the mammals and hence to us, so it is perhaps fitting that the plates should end with a portrait of a possible relative of our ancestor.

Pl.96   112

DINOSAUR CANCELLATIONS

A small selection of the many cancellations used for commemorative and other purposes, and an example of a dinosaur pre-print.

International Museum Day

Albuquerque Station

MAY 18, 1986

Albuquerque, New Mexico

THE DINOSAUR IS COMING!

CHRISTCHURCH N.Z. 20.7.38

NEW MEXICO MUSEUM OF NATURAL HISTORY GRAND OPENING JAN 11 1986 MUSEUM STATION ALBUQUERQUE, N.M. 87101

Veterans

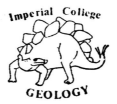

CHINESE DINOSAURS 17 JUNE - 31 JAN 88 Natural History Museum, London

LONDON 12.8.88 S.W.7.

IGUANODON BERNISSARTENSIS 1878 - 1978

Imperial College

GEOLOGY

LONDON 10. 4. 91 S.W.7.

An envelope pre-print used by the Institution Royal des Sciences Naturelles de Belgique.

DINOSAUR CIGARETTE AND TRADE CARDS

For the keen dinosaur collector, a few sets of cigarette cards of interest were published long before the first dinosaur stamp; two examples are given below.

A MONSTER OF THE SANDS

Ogden's 'The Story of Sand', 1934 - set of 50, no. 40 here features *Diplodocus*.

Stegosaurus (No. 21)

Hadrosaurus (No. 9)

Iguanodon (No. 11)

Edwards, Ringer & Bigg; 'Prehistoric Animals', 1924 set of 25 of which four with dinosaurs are shown here.

Triceratops (No. 25).

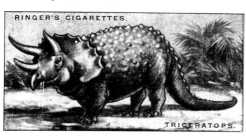

Trade cards have come into their own since the demise of cigarette card issues. Two particularly fine sets with albums are worthy of note, both published by Brooke Bond in the early 1960s - 'Prehistoric Animals', a U.K. set of 50 issued with tea, text by Dr Alan Charig, and 'Dinosaurs', a Canadian set of 50 issued with tea, coffee and baking powder, text by Dr W.E. Swinton.

A CHECKLIST OF KNOWN ISSUES WHICH INCLUDE DINOSAURS ON STAMPS

The term 'Dinosaur' is interpreted in its strict sense here (see the classification on pages 117-120) and excludes non-dinosaurian reptiles, and cartoon dinosaurs. The number of dinosaur stamps is shown in column 4. Where a country has issued the same design in two different values (surface and air) this is counted as one stamp only. To date there are 176 dinosaur stamps, in 55 sets from 44 countries/states.

This list is given in date order as far as practicable, however there are certain problems inherent in compiling a list such as this which should be borne in mind: With some countries the date of issue may be published and indeed printed on the stamps but for some reason or other the set may not actually be issued until the following year; in addition the date of issue may be incorrectly given in the stamp catalogue from which the data is taken, or the set may not be catalogued yet.

DATE	COUNTRY/ STATE	PLATE	STAMPS	DATE	COUNTRY/ STATE	PLATE	STAMPS
1958	China	23	1	1984	Benin	12	2
1965	Poland	68	6		Losotho	53	3
	San Marino	79	6		Mali	56	2
1966	Belgium	12	1		Vietnam	90	5
	Mongolia	59	4	1985	Cuba	26	6
1968	Aden	9	2	1986	Kampuchea	46	2
	Fujeira	31	4	1987	Cuba	27	5
1970	Congo	25	2		Guinea	38	3
	Lesotho	51	4		Nicaragua	66	1
	U.S.A.	87	1	1988	Afghanistan	10	4
1971	Yemen Rep.	93	1		Central African		
1972	Fujeira	32	4		Republic	21	8
	Maldives	55	4		Laos	48	5
	Manamar	57	6		Malagasy	54	4
1975	Congo	25	2		Morocco	65	1
1976	Niger	67	1		Tanzania	81	3
1977	Mongolia	60	1	1989	Guinea-Bissau	40	3
1978	Dahomey	28	2		Tonga	84	1
	Equatorial				U.S.A.	88	3
	Guinea	29	6	1990	Bulgaria	18	4
1979	Vietnam	89	5		East Germany	34	5
1980	Dhufar	28	1		Hungary	41	3
	Korea				Mongolia	60	8
	(North)	47	2		Russia	71	1
	Oman	67	2		Vietnam	92	4
	Poland	71	1		Yemen Rep.	94	1
1982	Kuwait	47	1	1991	British Antarctic		
	St Thomas &				Territory	15	1
	Prince	72	5		Great Britain	1	5
	South Africa	79	1		Tanzania	81	7

CUMULATIVE SETS OF DINOSAUR STAMPS ISSUED 1958 - End June 1991

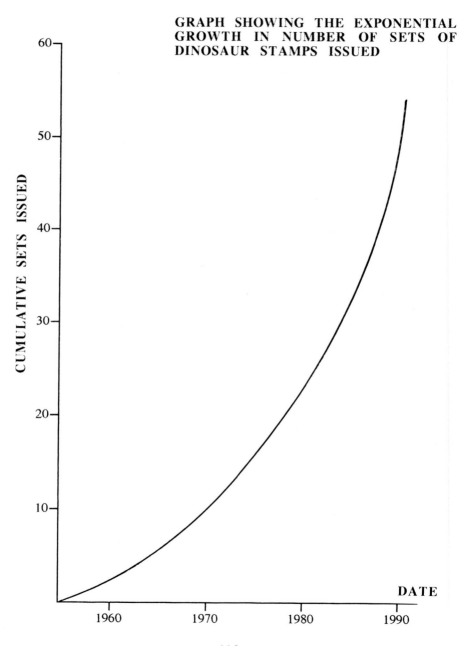

GRAPH SHOWING THE EXPONENTIAL GROWTH IN NUMBER OF SETS OF DINOSAUR STAMPS ISSUED

CLASSIFICATION OF AMPHIBIANS & REPTILES

CLASS AMPHIBIA

SUBCLASS LABYRINTHODONTIA

ORDER ICHTHYOSTEGALIA
Family Ichthyostegidae: *Ichthyostega*

ORDER TEMNOSPONDYLI
Family Capitosauridae: *Mastodonsaurus*

ORDER ANTHRACOSAURIA
Family Seymouridea: *Seymouria*

SUBCLASS LEPOSPONDYLI

ORDER NECTRIDEA
Family Keraterpetontidae: *Diplocaulus, Diploceraspis*

CLASS REPTILIA

SUBCLASS ANAPSIDA

ORDER CAPTORHINIDA
Family Protorothyrididae: *Hylonomus*
Family Pareiasauridae: *Bradysaurus*

ORDER MESOSAURIA
Family Mesosauridae: *Mesosaurus*

SUBCLASS TESTUDINATA

ORDER CHELONIA (turtles, tortoises and terrapins)
SUBORDER CRYPTODIRA
Family Dermatemydidae: *Mongolemys*

SUBCLASS UNCERTAIN

ORDER PLACODONTIA
Family Cyamodontidae: *Placochelys*

ORDER PLESIOSAURIA
Family Plesiosauridae: *Plesiosaurus*
Family Cryptocleididae: *Cryptoclidus*
Family Thaumatosauridae: *Thaumatosaurus*
Family Elasmosauridae: *Elasmosaurus, Wellesisaurus*

SUBCLASS DIAPSIDA

ORDER ICHTHYOSAURIA
    Family Ichthyosauridae: *Ichthyosaurus*
    Family Stenopterygiidae: *Stenopterygius*

SUPERORDER LEPIDOSAURIA

ORDER SQUAMATA (snakes and lizards)
SUBORDER LACERTILLIA (lizards)
    Family Mosasauridae: *Angolosaurus, Mosasaurus,*
        Tylosaurus
    Family Simoliophidae: *Pachyophis*

RULING REPTILES

INFRACLASS ARCHOSAUROMORPHA
SUPERORDER ARCHOSAURIA

ORDER THECODONTIA (thecodontians)
SUBORDER ORNITHOSUCHIA
    Family Euparkeriidae: *Euparkeria*
    Family Erpetosuchidae: *Saltoposuchus*

ORDER PTEROSAURIA (pterosaurs)
SUBORDER RHAMPHORHYNCHOIDEA
    Family Dimorphodontidae: *Dimorphodon*
    Family Rhamphorhynchidae: *Rhamphorhynchus, Sordes*

SUBORDER PTERODACTYLOIDEA
    Family Pterodactylidae: *Pterodactylus*
    Family Ornithocheiridae: *Pteranodon*

ORDER SAURISCHIA ('lizard-hipped' dinosaurs)
SUBORDER THEROPODA
INFRAORDER COELUROSAURIA
    Family Compsognathidae: *Compsognathus, Ornitholestes*
    Family Ornithomimidae: *Ornithomimus*

INFRAORDER CARNOSAURIA
    Family Megalosauridae: *Megalosaurus*
    Family Allosauridae: *Allosaurus*
    Family Ceratosauridae: *Ceratosaurus*
    Family Tyrannosauridae: *Albertosaurus (= Gorgosaurus),*
        Tarbosaurus, Tyrannosaurus

SUBORDER SAUROPODOMORPHA
INFRAORDER PROSAUROPODA

Family Plateosauridae: *Gryponyx, Lufengosaurus,*
Massopondylus, Plateosauravus,
Plateosaurus

INFRAORDER SAUROPODA

Family Cetiosauridae: *Cetiosaurus*
Family Brachiosauridae: *Brachiosaurus, 'Supersaurus',*
'Ultrasaurus'
Family Camarasauridae: *Ophistocoelicaudia*
Family Diplodocidae: *Apatosaurus (= Brontosaurus),*
Dicraeosaurus, Diplodocus,
Mamenchisaurus

ORDER ORNITHISCHIA ('bird-hipped' dinosaurs)
SUBORDER ORNITHOPODA

Family Fabrosauridae: *Lesothosaurus*
Family Heterodontosauridae: *Hetrodontosaurus*
Family Pachycephalosauridae: *Stegoceras*
Family Hypsilophodontidae: *Dryosaurus, Dysalotosaurus,*
Hypsilophodon
Family Iguanodontidae: *Camptosaurus, Iguanodon,*
Ouranosaurus, Probactrosaurus
Family Hadrosauridae: *Anatosaurus (= Trachodon),*
Corythosaurus, Edmontosaurus,
Parasaurolophus, Saurolophus

SUBORDER STEGOSAURIA

Family Stegosauridae: *Kentrosaurus, Stegosaurus*

SUBORDER ANKLYOSAURIA

Family Nodosauridae: *Hylaeosaurus, Silvisaurus*
Family Ankylosauridae: *Anklyosaurus, Euoplocephalus*
(= Scolosaurus), Talarurus

SUBORDER CERATOPIA

Family Psittacosauridae: *Psittacosaurus*
Family Protoceratopidae: *Protoceratops*
Family Ceratopidae: *Centrosaurus, Chasmosaurus,*
Monoclonius, Styracosaurus,
Torosaurus, Triceratops

MAMMAL-LIKE REPTILES
SUBCLASS SYNAPSIDA

ORDER PELYCOSAURIA
    Family Edaphosauridae: *Edaphosaurus*
    Family Sphenacodontidae: *Dimetrodon*

ORDER THERAPSIDA
SUBORDER DINOCEPHALIA
    Family Tapinocephalidae: *Moschops*

SUBORDER GORGONOPSIA
    Family Rubidgeidae: *Rubidgea*
    Family Inostranceviidae: *Sauroctonus*

SUBORDER DICYNODONTIA
    Family Endothiodontidae: *Emydops, Endothiodon*
    Family Dicynodontidae: *Oudenodon*
    Family Lystrosauridae: *Lystrosaurus*
    Family Stahleckeriidae: *Zambiasaurus*

SUBORDER CYNODONTIA
    Family Galesauridae: *Thrinaxodon*
    Family Cynognathidae: *Cynognathus*
    Family Tritylodontidae: *Tritylodon*
    Family Traversodontidae: *Luangwa*

The classification used here is based on the following sources:
Cox, B. et al. 1988; Norman, D. B. 1985 and Romer, A.S. 1966.

THE GEOLOGICAL COLUMN

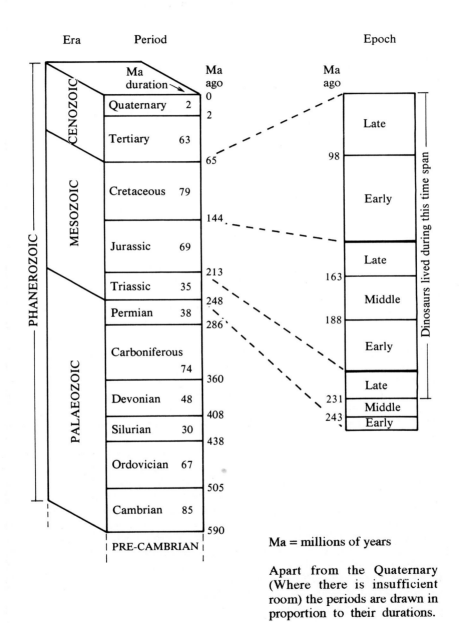

Ma = millions of years

Apart from the Quaternary (Where there is insufficient room) the periods are drawn in proportion to their durations.

REFERENCES AND SUGGESTIONS FOR FURTHER READING

BALDWIN, S.A. 1983. *Dinosaurs and their Relatives Project Pack for Schools*. For Primary and Junior Schools. Baldwin's Books, Witham, Essex. Still in print.

BARDEN, M. 1989. *How Royal Mail Special Stamps are Produced*. 28pp. Royal Mail, London.

BEARSE, G.A. et al. 1977. *Lower vertebrates: fishes, amphibia and reptiles on stamps of the World*. American Topical Association Handbook No. 91, 120pp.

BENTON, M.J. 1990. *The Reign of the Reptiles*. 144pp. Well illustrated.

BENTON, M.J. 1990. *Vertebrate Palaeontology*. xii, 377pp, many figures.

BITTER, P.H.von. 1977-78. Fossils in the Mail. *Rotunda* (Magazine of the Royal Ontario Museum) **10** (4), pp.4-11.

BROWN, R.W. 1979. *Composition of Scientific Words*. 882pp. Smithsonian Institution Press, Washington, D.C. An invaluable reference for palaeontologists.

CHARIG, A. 1983. *A new look at the Dinosaurs*. 160pp. Well illustrated.

COX, C.B. 1969. Two new dicynodonts from the Triassic Ntawere Formation, Zambia. *Bull B.M. (N.H.)* (Geology), **17**:(6), pp.255-294, figs.23.

COX, B.., SAVAGE, R.J.G., GARDINER, B. & DIXON, D. Macmillan. 1988. *Illustrated Encyclopaedia of Dinosaurs and Prehistoric Animals*. 312pp.

EDITIONS AV. 1991. *Catalogue de Timbre-Postes les Animaux du Monde Entier*. 1989-91, 18th edition. 440pp.

GARDINER, B.G. 1990-91. Clift, Darwin, Owen and the Dinosauria. *The Linnean*. Newsletter and Proceedings of the Linnean Society of London. 6(3), 19-27; 7(1), 8-14; 7(2), 13-20..

GIBBONS, S. 1991. *Stamps of the World*. Simplified Catalogue, 3 volumes.

GOULD, S.J. 1991. *Bully for Brontosaurus*. 540pp, illustrated. Hutchinson Radius.

HAILE, N.S. 1977. Geology on Stamps 1. Extinct Animals and Minerals. *Warta Geologi* (Newsletter of the Geological Society of Malaysia) 3(4), 47-50.

HAILE, N.S. 1977. Geology on Stamps 2. More Extinct Animals, Fossils and Minerals. *Warta Geologi*, 3(4), 71-76.

KEMP, T.S. 1980. Aspects of the structure and functional anatomy of the Middle Triassic cynodont *Luangwa*. *J.Zool.*, Lond. 191. 193-239

LONDON CIGARETTE CARD CO. 1981. *The Complete Catalogue of British Cigarette Cards*. 224pp.

HALSTEAD, L.B. & HALSTEAD, J. 1987. *Dinosaurs*. 170pp, many illustrations.

MANNING, P. 1979. *Earth Sciences on Stamps*. 15pp. Printed privately.

MANNING, P. Geological Postage Stamp Errors. Philagems. (c.1979).

NORMAN, D.B. 1985. *The Illustrated Encyclopaedia of Dinosaurs*. 208pp. Salamander, London. In print and one of the best dinosaur books written to date.

NORMAN, D.B. 1991. *Dinosaur*. 198pp. Boxtree Publications, London. The book accompanying the ITV television series first shown in the UK, Autumn 1991.

ROMER, A.S. 1966. *Vertebrate Paleontology*. 3rd edition. x, 468pp.

RUSSELL, D.A. 1989. *The Dinosaurs of North America*. 240pp. Well illustrated.

TURNER, J.R.G. 1967. The Evolution of the Vertebrates; Ancestors in the Mail. *Gibbons Stamp Monthly*. October 1967, 28-30.

ZHIMING, D. 1987. *Dinosaurs from China*. 114pp. Many illustrations.

INDEX OF GENERA

Neocalamites	87	*Styracosaurus*	10,27,29,57,68,90
Nothofagus	15,17	*'Supersaurus'*	53

Neocalamites 87
Nothofagus 15,17

Opisthocoelicaudia 61
Ornitholestes 39
Ornithomimus 39
Oudenodon 96
Ouranosaurus 67

Pachyophis 95
Parasaurolophus 72
Placochelys 41
Plateosauravus 51
Plateosaurus 23,31,39,47,51,57
81,82
Plesiosaurus 89
Probactrosaurus 61
Protoavis 33
Protoceratops 3,8,10,18,59
Psittacosaurus 60
Pteranodon 6,9,26,29,37,39
49,55,58,66,73,77
81,87,90
Pterodactylus 33

Rhamphorhynchus 9,18,28,29,46,50
69,83,87,90
Rubidgea 96

Saltoposuchus 28
Sauroctonus 45
Saurolophus 27,54,59,71
Scolosaurus 39
Seymouria 91
Silvisaurus 83
Sinomegaceros 24
Sordes 71
Stamposaurus 87
Stenopterygius 73
Stegoceras 4
Stegosaurus 2,4,6,8,10,18,21
25,26,28,29,31,32
38,39,40,41,42,47
54,55,57,60,68,72
73,74,77,81,84,87
89

Styracosaurus 10,27,29,57,68,90
'Supersaurus' 53

Talarurus 59
Tarbosaurus 41,46,59,61,71
Thaumatosaurus 77
Thrinaxodon 79
Torosaurus 4
Trachodon 9,48
Triceratops 3,4,6,8,18,21,27
29,31,32,39,54,55
56,66,67,72,77,81
90
Tritylodon 51
Tylosaurus 9,38,49,66
Tyrannosaurus 2,3,4,8,9,22,25,
27,28,37,39,40,41
47,48,54,55,68,72
74,77,78,89,92,94

'Ultrasaurus' 53

Wellesisaurus 43,44
Wielandella 87
Williamsonia 87

Zambiasaurus 95

GENERAL INDEX

Aden, 25,115
Afghanistan, 26,115
Age of Dinosaurs, 6,31
Age of Reptiles, 9
Alberta, Red Deer River Valley, 76
Algeria, 15
Ammonite(s), 15,32,51
Angola, 27
Antigua, 27
Archaeopteryx, 6
Archosaur, 49
Athenaeum, 7
Attenborough, Sir David, 4,12
Australia, 27
Barbuda, 27
Belemnites, 32
Belgian Royal Institute of Natural Sciences, Brussels, 28
Belgium, 28,29,115
Benin, 28,115
Berbericeras, 15
Berlin Museum of Natural History, 50
Bernissart, 28
Beverly Halstead Memorial Trust, 4
Bitter, P.H. von., 2,15,29,40,68,94,96
Brachiopod, 51
Bridgewater Treatise, 7
British Antarctic Territory, 30-33,115
British Association for the Advancement of Science, 7,14,128
British National Stamp Exhibitions, 14
Buckland, Rev William, 7
Bulgaria, 34,115
Burian, Z., 16,25,26,55,56,64,65,66
Canada, 35-36
Central African Republic, 37-38,115
Chang Qu, 39
China (People's Rep.), 15,39-40,115
Christmas, 12
Cocks, Dr Robin, 4
Commemorative Special Stamps, 12
Conference of European Postal and Telecommunications Administrations, 13
Congo (Brazzaville), 41,115
Conybeare, Dean, 59
Crocodiles, 7,49
Crystal Palace (Park), 9,17,21
Cuba, 42-43,115
Cuckfield, 7
Dahomey, 44,115

Darwin, Charles, 88
deinos, 7
Dhufar, 44,115
Dinner in the *Iguanodon*, 8,9
'Dino', 79
Dinosaur eggs, 19
Dinosauria, 2,7,17
Dinosaurs, 7,16,115
Edmonton, 98
Elephant(s), 15,38
Ellesmere Island, 35
Errors, 16
Essays, 13
Equatorial Guinea, 45-46,115
Europa, 12
Festival of Britain, 12
Fish, 32
Flintstones, 79,80,91,92
Forbes, Professor Edward, 9
Fujeira, 47-48,115
Geology Department, National Museum of Wales, 2,69,76
German East Africa, 50
Germany (East), 49-52,115
Gibbons, Stanley, 16
Glyptodon, 7
Gobi Desert, 19
Gondwana, 30,31
Graptolite, 51
Great Britain, 17-24,115
Greenland, 85
Grenada, 53
Guinea, 54-55,115
Guinea - Bissau, 56,115
Gurche, J., 16,78
Hadhramaut, 25
Hallett, Mark, 16,78
Halstead, Jenny, 2,13,128
Harrison & Sons (High Wycombe) Ltd, 13
Hawkins, Benjamin Waterhouse, 9,17,21
HM The Queen, 14
Holmes, Sherlock, 87
Holzmaden, 110
Horn Coral, 51
Howgate, Mike, 2,58,72
Hua Yang Guo Zhi, 39
Hungary, 57-59,115
Hylaeosaurus, 7,9,21
Ichthyosaur, 9,88
Ichthyosaurus, 11

125

THE AUTHORS

Stuart A Baldwin (1930 -   )

Was educated at Witney Grammar School followed by a varied career in electrical engineering (Crompton Parkinson), pharmacy (Bristol Royal Infirmary & the Wellcome Foundation) and computing (IBM). At the age of 28 he collected his first fossil and over the next ten years built up a collection of over 100,000 specimens. In 1969 this developed into a spare-time fossil replica manufacturing business. He was seconded by IBM to the London Enterprise Agency as Small Firms Adviser in 1979 and two years later took some of his own advice, leaving to start his own small firm - the dream of many - by converting his hobbies into a business.

He now runs a fossil replica manufacturing business, a museum of palaeontology, is a specialist dealer in secondhand books on geology and fossils, and writes and publishes books. His relaxations include collecting fossil stamps, lecturing, broadcasting and studying for an Open University degree.

L Beverly Halstead (1933 - 1991)

Geologist, vertebrate palaeontologist, author, popularizer of science, philosopher, editor, broadcaster, dinosaur expert and friend are but a few of the many ways in which this extraordinarily colourful character could be described. He was driven from within by a boundless and infectious energy which combined with his great personal charm left no one unaffected by his presence.

He held many university positions both in the U.K. and abroad, was a brilliant scientist and was greatly respected academically. He had an unusually wide range of interests and he also possessed that rare ability to communicate his knowledge and enthusiasm to the layman through the written and spoken word, including broadcasts both on radio and television. As President he brought a new style of leadership and instilled fresh vigour to the Geologists' Association of London.

He was a fighter for causes in which he had a strong belief, a trait which more than once brought him into conflict with entrenched opinion and authority. He had a passion for dinosaurs and in some 25 popular and scientific texts he communicated this passion in sales of over a million books world-wide. As President of the Geology Section of the British Association for the Advancement of Science's 150th anniversary meeting of the coining of the term 'Dinosauria' by Richard Owen, he had planned many special events. One of them involved him in growing his distinctive white hair for the last two years so he could appear as Owen and re-enact the famous scene of 150 years ago.

At his funeral, attended by hundreds, much was said by many in his honour. Two particular items come to mind: "You either loved Bev or hated him, but you couldn't ignore him" and as one who loved him I feel sure that Bev would have approved of the words attributed to him on his arrival in that other world: "Now look here God, about the extinction of the Dinosaurs......!".   SAB

THE DESIGNER

Jenny A Halstead

A medical and biological illustrator who has also specialized in dinosaurs. Together with her husband Bev, they produced numerous books on bones and dinosaurs including a series of books for children.